THE AMATEUR
ASTRONOMER'S
PATHFINDER

THE AMATEUR
ASTRONOMER'S
PATHFINDER

COLIN HUMPHREY

PHOTOGRAPHS FROM
THE SCIENCE PHOTO LIBRARY
LONDON

John Wiley & Sons

Chichester • New York • Brisbane • Toronto • Singapore

TO MY FATHER

First published in Great Britain 1992
by John Wiley and Sons Ltd,
Baffins Lane, Chichester,
West Sussex PO19 1UD, England

Published in the United States of America by:
John Wiley and Sons, Inc.,
605 Third Avenue,
New York, NY 10158-0012, USA

Published in Australia & New Zealand by:
Jacaranda Wiley Ltd,
33 Park Street, Milton Brisbane
Queensland 4064, Australia

ISBN 0-471-93452-6

Library of Congress Cataloging-in-Publication Data
is available from the Publishers on request.

British Library Cataloguing in Publication Data is
available from the British Library.

This book was conceived, edited, designed and produced by
Morgan Samuel Editions,
11 Uxbridge Street,
London W8 7TQ

Typesetting by Sprint Reproductions, London,
Separated, printed and bound by Toppan Printing Co (HK) Ltd, Hong Kong.

CONTENTS

I wonder why. I wonder why.
I wonder why I wonder.
I wonder why I wonder why
I wonder why I wonder!

RICHARD P. FEYNMAN

FOREWORD

HAD THE HUMAN RACE evolved on Venus there would be no books on astronomy, simply because there would be no subject called astronomy. Venus's atmosphere is so dense that there is no clear sky, so no starlight can penetrate the thick cloud cover and no planets can be seen.

Fortunately, on Earth the atmosphere is transparent – though how long it will remain so may depend on our attitude to pollution – and everyone, to some extent, has the opportunity to investigate the universe of which we are such an infinitesimally small part.

In fact, the amateur astronomer needs no specific training and very little investment. With just an inexpensive pair of binoculars and a book such as this, anyone from eight to eighty can qualify as an amateur astronomer.

With absolutely no equations or complex technical jargon, this book takes you on a guided tour of the Solar System. Each of our planetary neighbours is visited, and the guide shows how fascinating data and stunning photographs from the Voyager missions of the 1980s have given us a new perspective on space, undreamed of a mere 10 years ago. Then the tours continues – across our own galaxy, the Milky Way, and beyond.

Explicit, non-technical drawings, specially commissioned for this book, complement the text by helping us understand the basic laws of the universe, the life cycle of stars and awesome phenomena such as supernovae, quasars, pulsars and black holes.

But this book is not just intended to explain the facts of the cosmos and our fancies about it. It is also a highly practical sky watcher's guide. The entire sky is divided into manageable segments and each segment has its own large starchart, with accompanying text and photographs. These, together with notes on equipment and technique, prepare the newcomer of any age for an enthralling journey of discovery and wonder.

Each starry night beckons us to begin that journey – this book will help you to find your path.

An early representation of the Earth in the Universe, from *Harmonia Macrocosmica* 1660 by Cellarius.

HOW THE BOOK WORKS

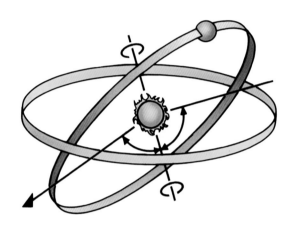

SECTION 1 — EARTH IN THE UNIVERSE

THE BEAUTY OF THE skies has enthralled observers for thousands of years. For much of that time there has been little or no understanding of the nature of the universe, and even today we are making startling discoveries that force us to question our beliefs. In the search for the origin of all things we are constantly changing our ideas about such problems as: how old is the universe?; how big is the universe?; what happened at its beginning?; and how will it all end? Before we can answer these questions we need to look at the universe as it is seen today and appreciate our place within it.

This section starts with a brief introduction to the

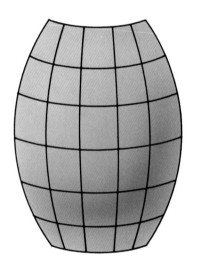

SECTION 2 — LOOKING AT THE NIGHT SKY

AS AN INTRODUCTION TO the way in which we map the skies, this section describes some of the basic rules and methods for describing the position of objects in the sky, as well as basic equipment for looking at them.

The starcharts themselves are accompanied by many photographs of some of the most beautiful of these objects, with descriptions of what can be seen and why the objects appear as they do.

At the end of the section you will find summary maps of the whole sky with lists of the constellations and where and when to observe them.

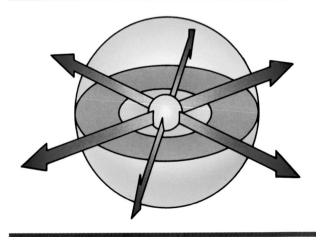

SECTION 3 — PROBING SPACE AND TIME

THE ORIGIN, EVOLUTION AND fate of the universe are some of the greatest unresolved mysteries facing modern science. This section looks at some of the methods used to explore these questions and describes the answers they are giving us.

The wide variety of giant ground-based telescopes, orbiting space telescopes and interplanetary probes provides vast amounts of information about the universe. The interpretation of this information, ranging from data about our own Sun to echoes of the Big Bang itself,

history of astronomy and the way in which views of the
universe have changed over the centuries. Next we look at
our current understanding of our place in the universe
and describe our nearest neighbours, the Moon, the Sun
and the planets. Moving out into space, we look at the
different objects – stars, nebulae, black holes – that make
up our galaxy, the Milky Way. Finally we move deeper
into space to see other galaxies and quasars, and describe
some of the past and present ideas about what is
happening in the universe.

increases our knowledge of the processes that created the
universe and will, it is hoped, allow scientists to predict
its evolution.

Daunting though some of the questions – and some of
the answers – are, you will find that you do not need a
scientific background to understand some of the
extraordinary conclusions astronomers have reached
about the intriguing nature of our cosmos.

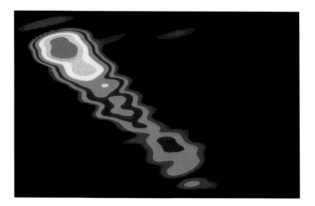

SECTION

EARTH IN THE UNIVERSE

THE STARTING POINT FOR our journey into the depths of time and space must be our own planet, the Earth. Without some understanding of Earth and its nearest neighbours in space, the Moon, the Sun and the planets, it is difficult to comprehend the nature of the night sky.

Star-gazers and astronomers have suffered from this lack of understanding for thousands of years. The ancient Babylonians realised that certain stars always appeared at the same time of year and used this knowledge to draw up calendars, but apart from this they achieved little other than to divide the sky into constellations.

Everyone thought the Earth was a flat disk, occupying its rightful position at the centre of the universe, with everything else revolving around it once a day. The great leap forward came with classical Greece, and the realisation that Earth was not flat but was, in fact, a sphere. This was demonstrated by the philosopher Aristotle, in the fourth century BC.

He pointed out that the star Polaris, the Pole Star, which hardly moves at all in the sky, appears to be higher in the sky if you go north and lower if you go south. The only conclusion was that the Earth was a globe and not flat. This idea was fairly conclusive and so, at last, it seemed that astronomy was really getting going. Or at least it should have been.

Around the turn of the fourth century BC, some Greeks did suggest that the Earth was going round the Sun, but nobody took much notice and the Earth stayed where it was. This was a bit of a shame because it meant that people had completely the wrong idea about what was going on "up there" for the next thousand years or so.

The main thing to remember here is that humans considered themselves, or more precisely the Earth, to be the result of divine creation. This naturally meant that they were at the centre of the universe and that everything in the heavens was perfect, by definition.

So the idea persisted that everything went round the Earth, and in the second century AD, another Greek philosopher, Ptolemy, really went to town and drew up an entire "cosmological model" for the universe. In simple terms this meant that he thought he knew where everything was in the universe (actually, he hadn't worked out the model completely, but published it anyway).

The Ptolemaic system, as it became known, described the universe as something similar in shape to an onion, but rather larger. I don't suppose Ptolemy mentioned a great deal about onions, but the simile gives a good idea of its structure if not the size. The notion went like this: the Earth was a globe at the centre of the universe (or the onion), the Moon, the Sun, and the five planets known at that time were each fixed to a sphere (the layers of the onion) and all the stars were fixed on a single sphere (the outer layer).

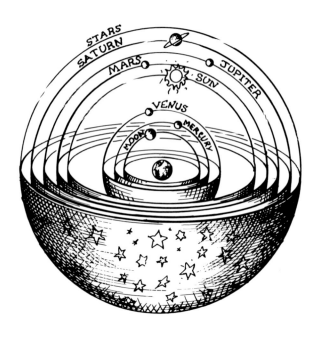

The Ptolemaic system had the Earth at the centre of an onion-shaped universe.

While these misconceptions remained there was no chance of discovering how the universe actually works.

The next development in the history of astronomy occurred in the Arab world during the eighth century AD, when Ptolemy's work was translated into Arabic. Work continued in the Middle East until the 15th century when the last major Arab astronomer, Ulugh Beigh, was murdered by his son, who had been banished on astrological advice – so much for astrology – so ending the Arab school of astronomy. During this period, returning Crusaders had taken a trickle of information home; later, the trickle became a flow of information about Arabic astronomy and the science of the ancient Greeks. And so the astronomy of Aristotle and Ptolemy came to be inflicted on Renaissance Europe.

When doubt was finally cast on the Ptolemaic system it came, ironically, from a member of the Church. In the early 16th century a Polish priest, Nicholas Copernicus, suggested that if the Sun and Earth were to swap places then the theory fitted the facts far better than in the Ptolemaic system. Not surprisingly, Copernicus was wary

The great leap forward in astronomy came when Nicholas Copernicus (1473-1543) realised that the Earth goes around the Sun.

Each of the spheres revolved around the Earth in various complex ways, and that explained the whole thing. Only it didn't.

Ptolemy's system meant that everything should move around the Earth in perfect circles. But he was an extremely good observer and knew perfectly well that various heavenly bodies, notably the planets, moved in all sorts of ways that were inconvenient for his theory.

To account for these he added various fiddles to his system, and eventually got it to predict the motions of the planets and the spheres reasonably well.

Unfortunately, he was almost completely wrong.

An even more unfortunate thing was that the Ptolemaic system was later adopted by the Christian Church, which thought it fitted the idea of creation, mankind's unique position in the universe and the perfection of the heavens. Arguing with the Church in those days was somewhat more dangerous than driving down the wrong side of a motorway at night, with no lights. So for several centuries astronomy went nowhere.

The problems were manifold. The Earth was believed to be at the centre of the universe, when in fact it goes round the Sun; the Earth was thought to be something special, when it is actually only a planet, like Mercury, Venus, Mars and so on; and because everything in the heavens had to be perfect, it followed that all objects in the sky had to move in perfect circles, which they don't.

Tycho Brahe

Tycho Brahe (1546-1601), one of the finest observational astronomers of all time, carried out his work before the advent of the telescope, using such instruments as this armillary. Brahe worked after Copernicus, but was still convinced that the Earth was at the centre of the Universe. However, it was Brahe's meticulous observations that allowed his assistant, Johannes Kepler, to prove that the planets do indeed move around the Sun.

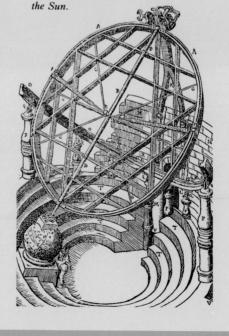

The scheme of Earth in the universe as described by Copernicus.

of making too much noise about all this: taking the Earth from its pre-eminent position and moving it to the lowly one of a planet revolving around the Sun would probably have resulted in him being excommunicated by the Church, and would certainly have limited his chances of promotion. As expected, his work was not generally accepted and was only published – in a work called *Concerning the Revolutions of the Celestial Bodies* – just before his death.

Not much changed during the 16th century and indeed the most widely respected observer of the day, Tycho Brahe, didn't believe Copernicus anyway. Tycho's observations of the stars and planets were the most accurate ever to have been made, and he realised that the existing theories, including those of Copernicus, gave rise

to insurmountable errors when it came to predicting the motion of heavenly bodies. He produced his own system for these motions, but unfortunately he put the Earth back at the centre of the universe – in fact, it was a giant step backward for mankind.

However, when Brahe died in 1601 he left his catalogue of observations to an assistant, Johanes Kepler. This was the first good news for astronomy since the days of Aristotle. Kepler was a mathematician and used Brahe's observations to show that if the Sun was at the centre and the planets moved around it in a kind of squashed circle (called an ellipse) then everything looked pretty good. At this time he also produced the three laws of planetary motion that are still accepted today.

Predictably, the Church was rather put out about all

Sir Isaac Newton

Sir Isaac Newton (1642-1747). One of the greatest scientific minds of all time, Newton developed a new type of telescope, which still bears his name: the Newtonian Reflector. This design is still used as the basis of many modern professional telescopes, and is popular with astronomers because it collects large amounts of light and allows the observer to see deep into the universe.

this, but when Galileo Galilei (who didn't actually invent the telescope – that was Hans Lippershy in Holland) used a telescope in 1609, he found various things in the sky, notably the moons of Jupiter, the phases of Venus, and the cratered surface of the Moon, that were awfully difficult to explain under the Ptolemaic system.

By himself Galileo was no great threat to the Church, but, as his ideas spread across Europe, opposition to the old notions was growing. In the century from the death of Copernicus in 1543 to the death of Galileo in 1642, there had been a revolution in astronomy that was to change our views of the universe forever.

The work of Kepler and Galileo finally put an end to the "Earth at the centre of the universe" idea, and the Copernican system, with a few minor changes, rapidly began to gain ground.

By the end of the 17th century, following the theoretical work on planetary motion by Sir Isaac

Newton, the Ptolemaic system was dead. Newton was born in the year of Galileo's death, and made many fundamental contributions to modern science. His work on the theory of gravitation was vital, and confirmed Kepler's third law of planetary motion. He developed a new type of telescope that employed a mirror to collect light instead of a lens. He showed, by shining it through a prism, that the "white" light of the Sun is made up of all the colours of the rainbow – this was the basis of a modern astronomical instrument called a spectroscope. He also created the calculus – a branch of mathematics that is essential to modern scientists.

At last astronomy was on the road again, and mathematicians and observers all over Europe turned their attention to the skies. But the most important steps had been taken. Astronomers could now observe the Solar System with some understanding of what they were looking at. The way to the stars was opening.

BASIC TERMS AND CONCEPTS

AS WITH ALL SCIENCES, astronomy abounds with technical terms and concepts. It is not necessary to understand all the scientific jargon in order to appreciate the wonders of the skies. However, there are a few fundamental pieces of information (and a few misconceptions) that do require an explanation.

LIGHT

We are all familiar with light in its most obvious forms: light from the Sun; light from a lamp in our homes; light from our car headlights. For most purposes there is no need to consider it any more deeply, but to astronomers an understanding of light in its various forms is the key to working out what is happening in the universe.

4.3 years to reach us here on Earth, so we say that the star is 4.3 light years away from us. The reason for doing this is that distances in terms of light years give much easier numbers to handle than the equivalent in kilometres, in this case 4.3 light years instead of about 25 million million miles (40MMkm).

So remember, light takes time to travel from one place to another and a light year is a measure of distance, *not time*. It is the distance that light travels in one year, which is equal to about 5.87 million million miles (9.46MMkm) For the rest of this book we will be giving astronomical distances measured in light years.

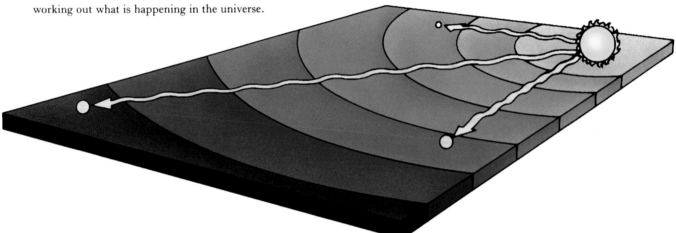

LIGHT YEARS AS A MEASURE OF DISTANCE

Consider the example of light coming from a lamp at home: when we switch on the lamp we expect the whole room to be lit immediately, and as far as we can tell it is. But this is not really true. When the lamp is switched on the light takes a very small amount of time to reach the walls of the room – the light has to travel the distance from the bulb to the walls. Because light travels so fast – 186,000 miles per second (299,793 km/s) – we don't notice the time between the light leaving the lamp and reaching the walls. But when the distances between the source of the light and the receiver are very much greater, as is the case of the distances between stars, then there is a very noticeable time delay, which can be used as a measure of the distance between the two.

Now here comes one of the greatest misconceptions in astronomy: the term "light year". This is frequently used when talking about the distances between objects in space. As we have said, light takes a certain amount of time to travel through space. If we measure this amount of time, we can describe the distance between the objects in terms of this "light-time". For example, the nearest star, apart from the Sun, is so far away that its light takes

Light from the Sun takes time to travel to the planets. In the case of the three innermost planets of the Solar System, for example, the Sun's rays reach Mercury in a little over 3 minutes; Venus in 6 minutes; and the Earth in just over 8 minutes.

LIGHT ISN'T WHITE

When Sir Isaac Newton performed his famous experiments with light in the 17th century, he showed that sunlight is made up of many different colours. He shone a ray of sunlight into a prism (a triangular block of glass) and out the other side came all the colours of the rainbow. This rainbow of colours is what is called the "visible spectrum", and contains the colours red, orange, yellow, green, blue, indigo and violet. It is only when all these colours are combined that the result is "white" light.

The reason for referring to this as the visible spectrum is that the light we can see with our eyes is just a part of a much larger spectrum, most of which is invisible to us.

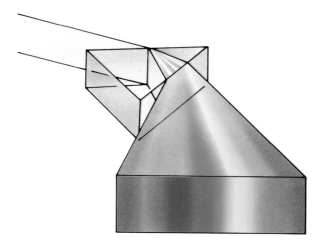

When reflected through a prism, white light can be seen to be composed of the colours of the visible spectrum: red, orange, yellow, green, blue, indigo and violet.

This larger spectrum is known as the "electromagnetic spectrum" and includes such things as radio waves, infra-red radiation, ultra-violet radiation, X-rays and gamma rays. These are collectively known as "electromagnetic radiation" and differ from light only in the amount of energy they possess.

We shall look more closely at the electromagnetic spectrum in Section 3 (*see pp114-5*), but for now all you need to know is that light is just one part of a whole range of radiations, all of which are the same in principle. The only reason we think of visible light as a special case is that it is easier to observe than the other types of radiation.

TIME AND DISTANCE

We have discussed the concept of light travelling and the time it takes to go from one place to another. This has a very important implication for astronomy, because the distances involved are so great. We see objects either by the light they emit, as with the Sun, or by the light they reflect, in the case of the Moon. The Moon is about 236,000 miles (380,000km) away from the Earth and light takes about one and a third seconds to travel this distance, so when we look at the Moon we see it not as it is now, but as it was one and a third seconds ago – we are looking into the past!

Now this may not seem to be terribly important, but consider what it means for all the objects we see in the sky: if we look at the nearest star, which is 4.3 light years away, we are looking 4.3 years back in time; if we look at the nearest major galaxy, outside our own, we are looking some 2.3 million years back in time; if we look at the most distant quasars we may be looking back in time as far as 15 thousand million years – back to a time just after the origin of the universe itself!

It is important to remember that we see objects in the sky by the light that has come from them, and that this light has taken a certain amount of time to travel the distance between them and us. So we see objects as they

were when their light left them and not as they are now – indeed some of the more distant objects probably don't exist any more, and others have certainly changed considerably in the interim.

The importance of all this for astronomers is that objects such as quasars, which existed long ago when the universe was very different, can be seen today and can give us an indication of what was going on back in the early stages of the universe.

GRAVITY

In the latter half of the 17th century various European scholars had been trying to explain why the planets go round the Sun and why they stay in these orbits. Again it was Sir Isaac Newton (and possibly others) who came up with the correct answer: there had to be a force of attraction between the planets and the Sun which keeps everything in place. This force was named gravity, and seemed to be a natural property of everything.

The idea is said to have come to Newton at his home when he saw an apple fall from a tree. This made him think that perhaps there was a force that acted between the apple and the Earth. He went further with this idea and realised that this force, gravity, was the same as the force that kept the planets in their orbits around the Sun.

In fact, everything in the universe, no matter how large or small, seems to attract everything else in the universe. The strength of the force between objects is directly related to how big they are (their mass) and the distance between them.

The concept of gravity is fundamental to the universe. Without it the universe, as we see it today, could not have formed. All of the planets, stars, galaxies and black holes that exist today came into being because the force of gravity caused very small particles of matter to stick together to form them, and keep them together once they had formed. The key fact to remember is this: as more and more particles of matter come together, because of the attractive force of gravity, their "gravitational field" (the strength of the attraction) increases. As we shall see in Section 3 (*see pp122-5*), this is why black holes form.

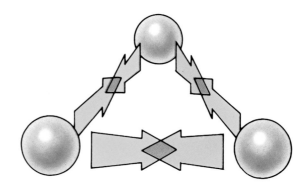

All objects in the universe have a mutual attraction due to the force of gravity – this is what keeps planets in their orbits.

WHERE WE ARE

AS WE HAVE SEEN, ancient peoples believed that the Earth was at the centre of the universe and that everything in the universe revolved around the Earth. Now we know that the situation is very different.

Any attempt to explain the universe around us must begin with an understanding of the structure of that universe and our own position within it. Although we still have many unanswered questions about what we see in the skies, we think we have a fairly good idea of the basic make-up of the cosmos around us.

We can explore the cosmos in six steps that take us from the Earth, out through space and into the depths of the universe. The illustrations below cannot be drawn to scale – there isn't enough room on the page – but with each step we jump further out into space to demonstrate the way in which objects are related to each other.

248,500 miles (400,000km). It's too small to have an atmosphere of its own and dead as the proverbial dodo, but it's ours and very important it is, too – without the Moon there would be no tides in the oceans, no spectacular eclipses of the Sun, and spacecraft would have a terribly long way to go to land on anything else.

So we have a companion traveller on our journey through space. Another familiar sight in the sky is the Sun, and every day we see the Sun rise in the morning and set in the evening, because the Earth is rotating.

The days are interrupted every now and then when the orbit of the Moon around the Earth causes it to get between us and the Sun, and we see an eclipse. So we view the Sun and Moon as almost exactly the same size in the sky, but is the Sun much further away than the Moon? When we see the Sun we are looking at a star, just like those thousands of others we can see on a clear night. Although it is only an average star, the Sun is well over one million times bigger than the Earth. To appear to be the same size as the Moon it must obviously be much further away – 93 million miles (150Mkm), in fact.

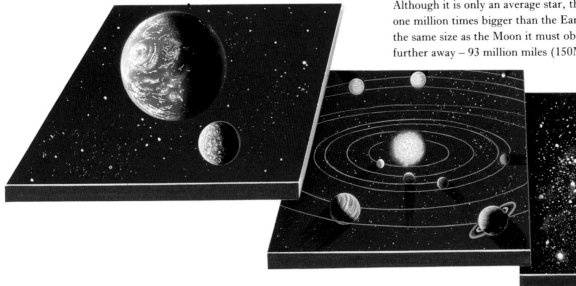

1. EARTH AND MOON

Most of us on Earth think that our planet is something special, and of course it is – to us. But this lump of rock we live on is really rather insignificant. Nevertheless it is the only planet in the Solar System that is hospitable enough to support the kind of life we know. It is just far enough from the Sun to be warm, but not too hot. It is just about the right size and composition to have an atmosphere that we can breath. We have our own natural satellite, the Moon. All-in-all we are fairly lucky to have such a desirable residence. But where are we in relation to everything else?

If we look at our nearest neighbour, the Moon, we see an object that is about one sixth of the size of Earth, going around us once a month, at a distance of just under

2. THE SOLAR SYSTEM

There are many more objects going around the Sun than just the Earth and Moon. Apart from Planet Earth there are eight others, some closer to the Sun, some further away; we are the third planet out from the centre. Many of these planets have their own natural satellites, or moons – one of the biggest planets, Saturn, has over 20 moons swirling around it.

But the Sun's family has many other members, too. Out between the orbits of the fourth planet, Mars, and the fifth planet, Jupiter, is a vast gulf that might appear empty. But this area holds tens of thousands of small rocky bodies called the minor planets, or asteroids, the largest of which is about 620 miles (1000km) across, though most of them are too small to be seen by all but passing spacecraft.

The most distant known planet from the Sun is Pluto, the ninth of the major planets. Out there in the icy depths, almost 3,750 million miles (6,000Mkm) from the Sun, there is little light and heat. A radio message home from a spacecraft at this distance would take over 5 hours to reach Earth, and the same time for the reply to return – not much of a conversation.

But Pluto is not the last member of the family, despite being 40 times further from the Sun than Earth. We have to travel deeper into space before we complete our tour of the Solar System.

3. BETWEEN THE STARS

Now we have reached a point so distant from the Sun that it appears no more than one of the brighter stars in the sky. Here, we believe, is the realm from which comets begin their enormous journey around the Sun. In a vast shell around the planets, this cometary cloud may stretch as far as 100 thousand times further than the distance from Earth to the Sun. So enormous are such distances that we measure them in the same way we measure the distance to stars – the edge of this cloud may be 2 light years away, almost half the distance to the nearest star.

This completes the roll call of the Solar System – the family of our Sun.

4. OUR GALAXY – THE MILKY WAY

Until now we have looked no further than our own doorstep astronomically speaking; only a couple of light years from home. Moving away from the Sun we would see dense fields of stars stretching across the sky and the Sun disappearing against the background. Now we jump far, far out into space, past those star fields, so that we see the sky on a much larger scale. We are now some 50 thousand light years from Earth. Below we see a vast spiral cloud. But this is not a cloud like any we have ever seen before – this is a galaxy, our galaxy, the Milky Way.

What we see is one of the most spectacular sights in the universe – an island in space, more than 100 thousand light years across, a gigantic collection of over 100 thousand million stars.

5. THE LOCAL GROUP OF GALAXIES

From our viewpoint just outside our galaxy the rest of the sky would be drowned by the light of that fabulous spiral, but now we move further out, into inter-galactic space. The Milky Way is not the limit of the universe – other star systems, some of them similar to our own, begin to appear. The distance between the larger members of the group is millions of light years but they are still neighbours in terms of the scale of the cosmos. Our galaxy is just one of a cluster of both large and small galaxies – the Local Group.

6. INTO THE VOID

If we travel yet further into the vast open spaces between the galaxies, we begin to realise that many groups of galaxies exist and these in turn are related to form superclusters of galaxies. On this scale the structure is almost impossible to appreciate.

But there is more: at the very edge of the observable universe are objects we have never seen before. These are quasars, giant powerhouses that have shone since the beginning of the universe, 15,000 million years ago.

THE SOLAR SYSTEM

OUR STAR, THE SUN, and its family of nine planets, along with various asteroids, meteoroids and comets, makes up the small group of space travellers that we have named the Solar System.

The Sun is just one of over 100 thousand million stars in our galaxy, the Milky Way, and when we compare it to other stars it turns out to be very ordinary. Its size, temperature, brightness and mass are all average. Because of this, there is no reason to believe that other stars, similar to the Sun, do not have families of their own.

Over the past few decades we have discovered more and more about the origin of the Solar System. It seems probable that all star systems formed in much the same way as ours, explaining many of the similarities we expect to see between them.

If we look back to the origin of the universe, it is now generally accepted that all the matter that exists today started as one "lump". An enormous explosion, which astronomers call the "Big Bang", caused this lump of matter to expand rapidly, and as it expanded it cooled. The resulting vast cloud of gas broke up into many smaller clouds. Inside these clouds some areas were more dense than others and in these regions of higher density the gas began to collect together to form stars. In the case of our own galaxy, this happened about 10 thousand million years ago. But not all of the original gas condensed into stars – in some places it was too thinly spread out for star formation to begin.

So, for billions of years, the first stars in our galaxy shone. Then, as they ran out of fuel and began to die, some of the larger ones erupted in massive explosions called supernovae. These explosions caused some of the

Almost 5 billion years ago, the initial cloud of gas and dust began to collapse in the first stage of the formation of the Sun.

original left-over gas to become compressed and so started a new generation of star formation.

We now believe that our Sun and its planets were formed after just such a secondary event, about four and a half thousand million years ago. As the gas cloud became compressed the mutual gravitational attraction of all the particles within it caused it to shrink even further. In the centre of the cloud the density was highest, and gravity pulled the particles together to form a nucleus which, as it collapsed, became hotter and hotter. When the temperature reached about 10 million degrees the process of nuclear fusion began and the Sun was born. By now the initial cloud had become a flattened, rotating disk, with the Sun shining out like some huge celestial lighthouse at the centre.

The energy that flowed from this new star swept the nearby gas away, past the area in which the inner planets would soon begin to form. But there were still particles of dust and rock in this region, and these began to combine to form larger objects. As they moved around the Sun these lumps of rock swept up the smaller debris around them and grew into planets – four of them: Mercury, Venus, Earth and Mars. These are the "terrestrial" planets, small, hot and built of rock.

Much further out in the disk other objects were forming. But these were very different from the warm planets that now orbited close to the Sun. They were made of ice, not rock. These frozen worlds were much heavier than the inner planets, and as they collected

ABOVE Once the central mass had condensed sufficiently and the temperature reached 10 million degrees the Sun began to shine with its own light.

BELOW The final stage of formation of the Solar System: the condensation of the planets.

particles from the gas-rich areas far from the central star they became massive by comparison, only stopping growing when all of the free gas had been sucked in by their enormous gravity. These are the "Jovian" planets: Jupiter, Saturn, Uranus and Neptune – gas giants that dwarf the terrestrials.

This was not the end of the story. There were two regions in which other activity was occurring. Outside the orbit of Mars another planet was trying to form, but the massive gravitational pull of the next planet, Jupiter, would not allow it to condense. The result was the asteroid belt: vast numbers, perhaps hundreds of thousands, of small bodies of rock – "minor planets" or "planetoids" ranging in size from a few yards to 620 miles (1000km) in diameter. Meanwhile, in the outer reaches of the newly born Solar System, the smallest planet of all, Pluto, was forming and looking like a mixture of the others – a rocky snowball. From so far out in space, the Sun is just another star, slightly brighter than the rest.

But what lies beyond Pluto? The tenth planet? Light years of empty space? Nobody really knows, but this may be the region where comets wander in massive orbits, travelling in near-darkness until something dislodges one, for it to soar towards the Sun for a brief display of celestial pyrotechnics.

IN THE FOLLOWING PAGES we look at the individual members of the Solar System in more detail. Here is a brief overview at this family as a whole.

THE TERRESTRIAL PLANETS

The four inner planets – Mercury, Venus, Earth and Mars – are all small bodies, composed mainly of rock. The name "terrestrial" is derived from the Latin word *terra,* meaning the Earth.

THE MINOR PLANETS – THE ASTEROID BELT

These very small pieces of rock were probably formed during the original condensation of the Solar System, but did not coalesce to form a major planet because of the disruptive effect of Jupiter's massive gravitational field. They range in size from a few yards across to more than 620 miles (1000km). Although many are too small to be seen from Earth it is thought that there could be hundreds of thousands of such objects.

THE JOVIAN PLANETS

Planets five to eight are the "gas giants" – Jupiter, Saturn, Uranus and Neptune – so called because they have no solid surface but have massive gaseous atmospheres surrounding, it is thought, liquified and solid gas layers and, in the case of Uranus and Neptune, a large rocky core. They are referred to as Jovian from the Latin word *Jovialis,* meaning "of Jupiter".

PLUTO

The ninth planet is unlike any other in the Solar System. It is by far the smallest of the planets but has a moon that is the largest, in relation to the size of the planet, of any in the Solar System, and so forms what is effectively a double planet.

THE REALM OF THE COMETS

Well beyond the orbit of Pluto, in the vast reaches between the stars, is thought to exist an enormous shell of icy bodies that is the source of the comets. These objects remain in their distant orbits around the Sun until some chance encounter with an interstellar traveller causes them to head towards the inner Solar System. It is believed that this cloud of would-be comets may stretch as far as half way to the next star.

ORBITS OF THE PLANETS

When the Solar System formed from its initial interstellar gas, the process of condensation caused the cloud to form a flat rotating disk. As the Sun condensed in the centre of the disk the planets were slowly coalescing further out. The orbits the planets follow today are still, for the most part, in the plane of the original disk and so they appear to be going around on a giant turntable. The main exception to this is the planet Pluto, which has an orbit inclined to the plane of the rest, and is far more eccentric than the others. It is possible that Pluto was once a moon of Neptune and was thrown out of its orbit, although this is by no means certain.

The motion of the planets, and in fact all orbiting objects, is governed by the three laws of planetary motion, first stated by Johannes Kepler at the beginning of the 17th century. These are:

1. A planet moves in an ellipse with the Sun positioned at one focus.
2. A planet sweeps out equal areas within the ellipse, in equal times.
3. The orbital period squared is proportional to its average distance from the Sun, cubed.

The result of these laws is that it should be very simple to calculate the orbital position of a planet. Unfortunately the effect of gravitation causes the planets to disturb each others' motion and so the calculation becomes enormously more complicated, as was found by the astronomers who attempted to predict the positions of Uranus, Neptune and Pluto before their eventual discovery.

The four terrestrial planets – Mercury, Venus, Earth and Mars – occupy the warm inner region of the Solar System.

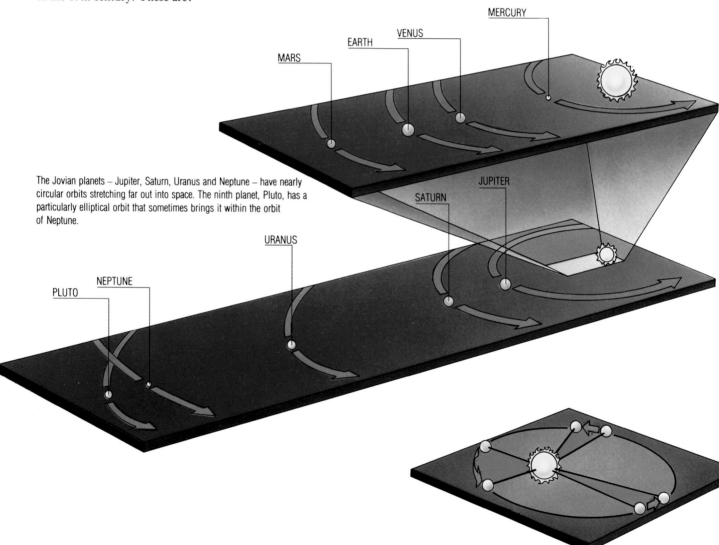

MERCURY

VENUS

EARTH

MARS

The Jovian planets – Jupiter, Saturn, Uranus and Neptune – have nearly circular orbits stretching far out into space. The ninth planet, Pluto, has a particularly elliptical orbit that sometimes brings it within the orbit of Neptune.

JUPITER

SATURN

URANUS

NEPTUNE

PLUTO

The red arrows represent equal periods of time in a planet's orbit. The areas between the planet and the Sun, marked in green, are equal over these periods of time, as stated in Kepler's 2nd law.

THE SUN

IT IS NOT SURPRISING that ancient civilisations believed the Sun to be something very special indeed – a god, in fact – because without its light and heat there would never have been any life on Earth. But today, even though it is vital to our survival, we know that the Sun is a normal star, and a very ordinary one at that. Nevertheless, it is the only star close enough for us to see any surface detail and gives a splendid opportunity for astronomical research. From observations of the Sun we can begin to understand the nature of the processes operating in other stars.

So what is a star? As we discussed earlier, stars form from massive clouds of gas. The gas is hydrogen, the lightest and most common element in the universe. As the hydrogen cloud contracts under the force of gravity, it heats up. When it reaches about 10 million degrees the individual atoms of hydrogen begin to combine to form the next lightest element, helium. In this process – called fusion, the same process that occurs when a hydrogen bomb explodes – energy is given out. This energy is what makes the star shine.

So a star is not actually burning, but operates by nuclear fusion reactions. But this process is exactly what causes a hydrogen bomb to explode, so why doesn't a star explode? For the answer, we have to look again at gravity. The individual atoms of hydrogen attract each other with a small, but significant, gravitational force. When we consider all the atoms in the cloud, the force is enormous – it is what caused the initial cloud to contract. So the star has two great forces acting on it; the outward pressure of the radiation from fusion, which tries to break it apart; and the inward pressure of gravity trying to crush it. When these two forces become equal, soon after the star is first formed, the star is said to have reached equilibrium, or, simply, to have become stable.

Our Sun has been in this state for over 4 thousand million years and will continue like it for a similar amount of time. But the process of fusion gradually uses up some of the matter (the mass) of a star, and so eventually things will have to change – what happens as a consequence of these changes is described overleaf, in a life story of the Sun. But for now let us look at the Sun as it exists today.

First of all, a word of warning. When Galileo first used his telescope to look at the Sun, he almost blinded himself in the process. Even looking at the Sun with the naked eye is dangerous, but using the optical equipment available today it is certain that you will damage your eyesight permanently. Don't take any notice of so-called "sun filters" – they don't work. If you want to look at the Sun, buy a properly made projection screen for your telescope.

At the centre of the Sun is the core – the region where the fusion of hydrogen into helium is taking place. This conversion of matter into energy causes the Sun to lose mass at a rate of about 4 million tons per second! It is thought that the temperature here is some 14 million

Physical Data	
average distance from Earth	93 million miles (150Mkm)
diameter	865,000 miles (1.4Mkm)
surface temperature (degrees C)	5,800 degrees

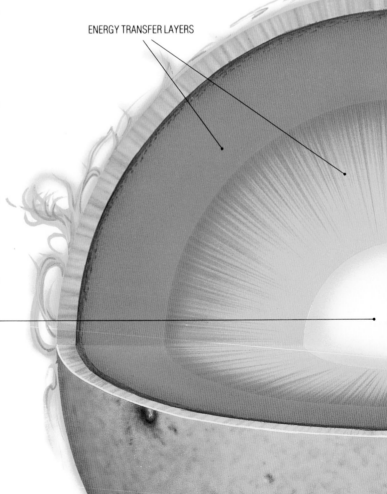

ENERGY TRANSFER LAYERS

CORE

Energy is generated in the core of the Sun and transported through the various layers to the surface by convection currents.

degrees. From the outer edges of the core there are
probably a number of layers in which heated gas
transports energy to the surface via convection currents.

As we know, the Sun is a giant ball of gas and so its
surface is not solid. What we see as the visible surface is
called the photosphere. This is the region where we
observe the dark features known as sunspots. These
"dark" areas are actually brighter than arc-lights but
appear black against the rest of the photosphere, which is
about 1,000 degrees hotter. Sunspots are thought to be
the result of magnetic fields that disrupt the surface with
a subsequent decrease in temperature. They are not
permanent features but increase and decrease on a regular
11-year cycle. Associated with sunspots, and often
appearing before them, are faculae – bright areas that
exist in the atmosphere above sunspots.

The atmosphere directly above the photosphere is
called the chromosphere and extends for a few thousand
miles into space. Above this is the corona – a region of
very low density that may stretch for millions of miles
away. It is within these layers that some of the most
spectacular events in the Solar System can be seen. These
are massive eruptions of gas from the surface, called
prominences, which can form giant arches stretching far
into the corona; they can be seen during total eclipses of
the Sun, at which time the bright photosphere is
obscured and the atmosphere becomes visible.

This beautiful "diamond ring" effect can
be seen at the start and end of a total eclipse. The
blue ring is the Sun's outer atmosphere, seen
against the black of the Moon's disk; the "jewel"
is part of the Sun's disk, not quite hidden.

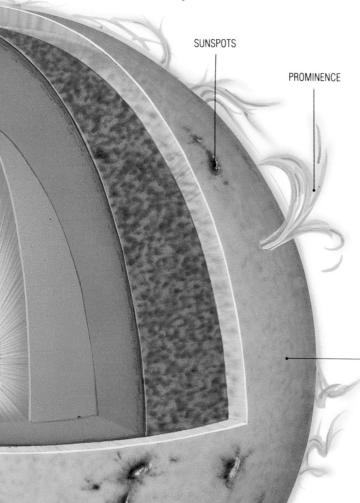

SUNSPOTS

PROMINENCE

PHOTOSPHERE

THE SUN – A LIFE STORY

As we have already seen, the Sun was formed from the collapse of a massive cloud of hydrogen. Some heavier elements, as well as particles of dust, were also in the initial cloud. These were the remnants of older stars that had exploded, but still the vast majority of the mass of the Sun was hydrogen.

The process of fusion, which generates the Sun's energy, converts the hydrogen into helium. This hydrogen fusion stage will last for a total of about 10 thousand million years from the birth of the Sun. After this time all of the hydrogen in the Sun's core will have been used up, but there will still be hydrogen in layers above the core and these will begin to fuse to form more helium. This process continues in successive layers out from the core, until a layer is reached where the temperature is less than about 10 million degrees – too cool for the reaction to continue – and fusion stops.

During this time the outward pressure of radiation has been decreasing, and so the force of gravity causes the entire star to contract. Meanwhile, the fusion of the layers of hydrogen has in effect caused the size of the core to increase – it begins to collapse under its own weight.

This collapse itself releases energy, causing the outer layers to stop shrinking and then to expand. The core, however, continues to contract and the temperature inside rises. Eventually the temperature reaches 100 million degrees, at which point helium itself begins to fuse to form carbon. This releases further energy, causing the Sun to shine again, with a limited new lease of life; it will also have caused a thin shell of hydrogen, far out from the core, to begin fusion again. The total outward pressure of radiation now becomes too much for the inward force of gravity and the outer layers suffer a rapid expansion and cooling – the Sun becomes a "red giant". So great is this expansion that the inner planets – Mercury, Venus and Earth – are swallowed up inside the star. By now, the Sun has evolved from an ordinary yellow star, 87,000 miles (140,000km), to a massive red giant of some 93 million miles (150Mkm) in diameter.

As the Sun swells toward the orbit of the Earth, the temperature here will rise dramatically; the polar ice caps will melt; the oceans will boil and eventually evaporate; the atmosphere will be swept away into space. Finally, the Earth will be reduced to a blackened cinder. Let us hope that by then, several thousand million years from now, humans have learned to travel between the stars and we will have left the Earth to its fiery fate.

The Earth may be doomed to an ignominious end, but the Sun will go out in a blaze of glory. As the helium in the core is exhausted and all that remains is carbon, the core will begin to contract again. The temperature will rise and the carbon will fuse together briefly to form oxygen. The Sun will become unstable; a series of expansions and contractions will occur as gravitational

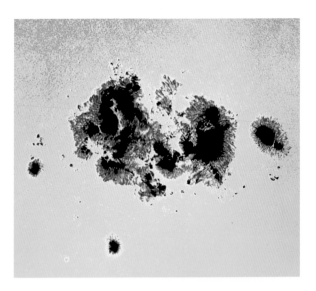

This group of sunspots only appears dark because it is some 1000 degrees cooler than the surrounding surface. The sunspots would look as bright as arc lights if they were seen on their own.

force fights radiation pressure for supremacy. Finally, the Sun's atmosphere will be ejected into space, expanding at tens of miles per second as a giant shell of gas. The naked core, at a temperature of perhaps 100,000 degrees, will pour radiation out into the cloud around it. The gas will light up and shine in the darkness of space – a planetary nebula, light years in diameter.

What is left of the original star will not be hot enough or massive enough to cause the fusion of heavier elements. As the carbon fuel runs out in the core the remnants will begin their final collapse and the Sun will become a white dwarf – a star no larger than the Earth itself. But with no other source of energy the Sun's remaining heat will slowly leak away into space, a dying ember, soon to become a black dwarf, cold and dead.

LEFT After its initial condensation out of a cloud of gas and dust, the Sun will evolve through various stages. It will stay as it is now, a normal yellow star, for several billion years, and then expand to become a red giant. After this relatively short stage, it will run out of fuel to produce energy and end its life as a white dwarf, cooling until all the energy is gone.

BELOW The arch on the Sun's surface, which stretches into the atmosphere, is a massive eruption of gas called a prominence.

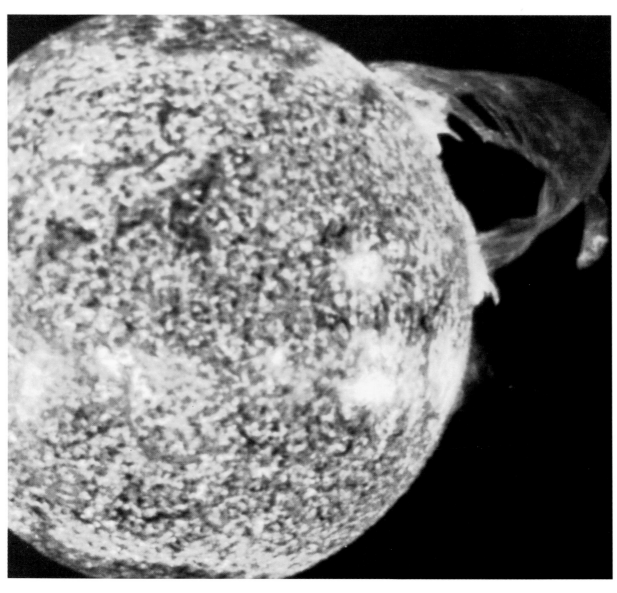

MERCURY

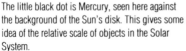
The little black dot is Mercury, seen here against the background of the Sun's disk. This gives some idea of the relative scale of objects in the Solar System.

RIGHT The surface of Mercury shown in a mosaic of photographs taken by the Mariner 10 spacecraft during its 1974 fly-past of the planet.

THE CLOSEST PLANET TO THE SUN, Mercury is always near to it in the sky and difficult to see. At its brightest it only appears as a relatively bright star. Even the largest telescopes show only faint markings on its surface.

Until as recently as 1965 it was thought that Mercury's period of rotation on its own axis was the same as its orbital period round the Sun (its year). This would have had the strange effect of making the day the same length as the year. Mercury would always have one face toward the Sun and on this side the temperature would be hot enough to melt metal, while the other would have been in permanent, icy winter. We have a good example of this on our doorstep – at any point in our moon's orbit the same side always faces Earth.

However, in 1965 the largest radio telescope in the world, the 1000ft (300m) natural dish at Arecibo in Puerto Rico, was used to study the rotation of the planet and it was discovered that Mercury actually rotates in just under 59 days – exactly two thirds of its year. This creates an effect even stranger than was originally

thought. The result is that one Mercurian "day" is actually two Mercurian "years" in length.

Another peculiarity of Mercury is an effect of the shape of its orbit. Kepler showed that all planets move around the Sun in an ellipse – a path something like a slightly flattened circle. Mercury has the second most elliptical orbit of any planet, next to Pluto. At the nearest point in its orbit Mercury is only two-thirds as far from the Sun as at its furthest point. As a planet comes closer to the Sun it has to travel faster in its orbit. When Mercury is at its closest point to the Sun it is travelling so fast that, to an observer on the planet, its speed appears to reverse the effect of its rotation – for a few hours at this point, the Sun seems to stop in the sky, go backwards, and then continue in its normal way.

Apart from the discoveries about its orbit and rotation, nothing much was known about Mercury until the Mariner 10 spacecraft was placed into an orbit around the Sun in 1974. This orbit allowed the spacecraft to pass Mercury on three occasions during the next year, and all

the information we now have about the planet comes from these observations.

The Mariner 10 photographs show the surface of the planet to be very similar to that of the Moon, being covered with craters that were formed by the impact of meteorites – debris left over from the creation of the Solar System. There are also highland areas and flat plains. A surprising fact, identified by Mariner 10, is that Mercury has a weak magnetic field. The implication is that there must be a liquid metallic core that represents a very large proportion of the planet and accounts for its relatively high density. There is confirmation of this in the Mariner 10 photographs – we see high ridges running for hundreds of miles across the surface of the planet, and it is thought that these were formed as the metallic core cooled and shrank, causing the crust above to wrinkle.

Despite its high density, Mercury is too small and hot to retain anything but the most transient atmosphere, and generally has little of interest that would make further visits likely in the near future.

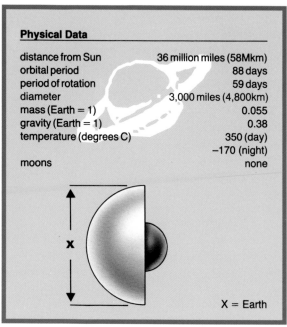

Physical Data

distance from Sun	36 million miles (58Mkm)
orbital period	88 days
period of rotation	59 days
diameter	3,000 miles (4,800km)
mass (Earth = 1)	0.055
gravity (Earth = 1)	0.38
temperature (degrees C)	350 (day)
	−170 (night)
moons	none

X = Earth

VENUS

SOMETIMES REFERRED TO AS EARTH'S TWIN, because of the similarity in size, mass and structure, Venus is still something of a mystery to us. Despite being the subject of visits by numerous spacecraft, the planet has such a dense and obscure atmosphere that relatively little is known of its surface.

The atmosphere itself has now been analysed and its composition is fairly well understood, but the reasons for the quantities of the various constituents still remain a puzzle. The relative amounts of the numerous elements it contains differ dramatically from those of Earth's atmosphere; in particular, carbon dioxide comprises about 97 per cent of the atmosphere of Venus, while much less than 1 per cent of Earth's.

It is this carbon dioxide which gives rise to the much-publicised "greenhouse effect" – a process that prevents infra-red radiation, from the Sun, escaping back into space and thus causing the planet to heat up. As a result of the enormous mass of carbon dioxide, the surface pressure is probably some ninety times that of the Earth, and this explains why so many spacecraft stopped sending information soon after they entered the atmosphere of Venus – they were crushed by the pressure.

But it appears that this strange atmosphere has not always been present. Today there is no water on the surface of Venus, or in its atmosphere, but it seems that there has been a substantial amount in the past – some elements are present in the atmosphere in such quantities that there would have to have been large bodies of water at some time, but the greenhouse effect caused them to evaporate long ago. The early presence of water leads to the possibility that life may have formed at some point in its past, but the temperature on Venus today is far too great for it to have survived.

Apart from some photographs from the Russian Venera spacecraft, most of our knowledge of the Venusian surface comes from surveys performed using radio waves, both by Earth-based radio telescopes and spacecraft. Radio waves can penetrate the atmosphere of Venus and allow us to "see" the major features such as craters, mountains and volcanoes.

When this technique was first used in 1962, astronomers were trying to discover the length of a "day" on Venus – the period of rotation. Yet again, Venus was full of surprises. The Venusian day turned out to be the longest in the Solar System and longer than its year, at 243 Earth days. But this is the time for the planet to rotate on its axis and, because the planet is moving around the Sun, the actual period between one sunrise and the next is 120 days.

But there was another surprise to come: Venus is rotating backwards. Most of the planets rotate in the same

LEFT This photograph of Venus was taken by an orbiting Pioneer spacecraft. It shows the dense carbon dioxide clouds that cover the surface and give rise to the greenhouse effect.

RIGHT The north polar region of Venus, showing the highest mountains on the planet's surface. This picture was compiled using radar techniques to penetrate the thick atmosphere.

direction, relative to the Sun, but not Venus. Further radio surveys of the planet have revealed the shape of the waterless surface. There appear to be no great ocean basins; Venus is flatter than Earth. Nevertheless there are mountain ranges – one mountain, Maxwell Montes, is higher than Earth's Mount Everest, at 7 miles (11km). Some of the major features of Venus seem to have been caused by volcanic activity, and volcanoes are almost certainly active today.

Pictures from the various Venera spacecraft show a barren surface of boulders and flat stones. Another surprise, on a planet with such a hostile atmosphere, is that these rocks are sharp and rough when we would have expected them to have been polished by great storms. In fact the winds at ground level turn out to be almost non-existent. A final treat for the Venus watchers – the Venera trips showed that the sky is orange.

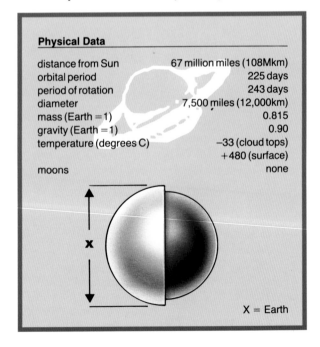

Physical Data

distance from Sun	67 million miles (108Mkm)
orbital period	225 days
period of rotation	243 days
diameter	7,500 miles (12,000km)
mass (Earth = 1)	0.815
gravity (Earth = 1)	0.90
temperature (degrees C)	−33 (cloud tops)
	+480 (surface)
moons	none

X = Earth

EARTH

AS WE SIT HERE on our home planet it is natural to think that we are living on a rather unusual world. But when we look at the other planets, especially the terrestrials, we see that Earth is only peculiar in having an oxygen-rich atmosphere and large areas of surface water.

Although it is difficult to study the interiors of other planets it is obvious that Venus and Mars, as well as some of the moons of the larger planets, have suffered from similar types of geological activity as Earth. They show evidence of plate tectonics, mountain formation, weathering and volcanic activity, all of which can still be seen on many worlds and continue to the present day. On the majority of the non-gaseous worlds there is evidence of large meteorite impacts. On Earth, these are most obvious in Arizona and Siberia; the only reason we see relatively few on our planet is that most have been eroded away over geological time.

Our atmosphere and oceans are only peculiar in that they contain large quantities of oxygen and water. Atmospheres are not uncommon on other planets and moons, the major difference being that of composition – often there are high concentrations of carbon dioxide, methane and ammonia. But polar ice caps – possibly of frozen carbon dioxide – can be seen on Mars and a number of moons.

The Jovian planets, the gas giants, have storms, though of far greater ferocity than those of Earth; many worlds, like us, also have magnetic fields. Even the Earth-Moon relationship that makes us appear almost as a double planet is not unique – Pluto's moon, Charon, is even larger in relation to its primary – and many worlds have numbers of natural satellites rather than just one.

So the Earth is superficially much the same as the other members of the Sun's family – or is it? Perhaps if we stand back and look at our planet we will begin to realise just how different it is.

A view of the Earth from space shows that our planet's surface is blue. But this is not the blue of the methane atmospheres that surround the gas giants, Uranus and Neptune. The blue of Earth is that of a surface covered with water – something that exists nowhere else in the Solar System, except as rock-hard ice. And what of the constituents of water: hydrogen and oxygen? How does our planet come to provide so much oxygen when it is all but non-existent on the rest of the planets?

The answer lies in something else which exists on no other planet of our family: vegetation. The plants that cover vast tracts of land around our globe absorb deadly carbon dioxide from the atmosphere and change it through photosynthesis, growing larger as they do so. But this is not the only benefit of greenery. In the process of converting carbon dioxide into food, plants release oxygen and in doing so give life to the planet.

Without the main areas of vegetation – the rain forests

LEFT An Apollo 17 photograph of the Earth, superimposed on a background of stars, shows Africa, Antarctica and Arabia, as well as swirling cloud systems.

RIGHT Different layers in the Earth's atmosphere create various effects at different heights, as well as being essential to our communication systems and protecting us from harmful Solar radiation.

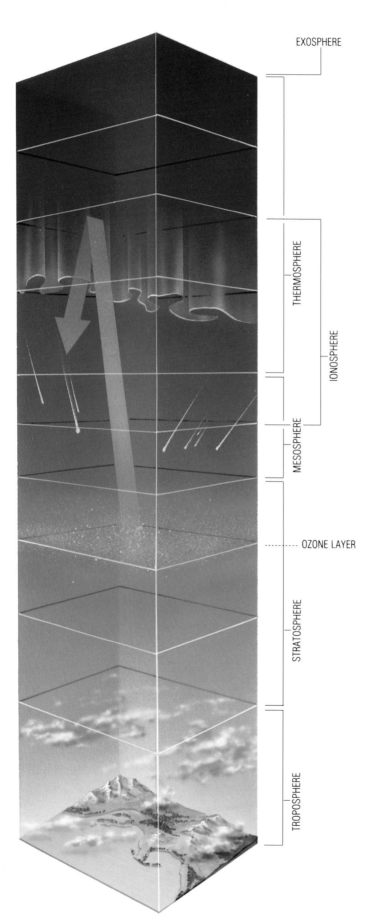

EXOSPHERE

THERMOSPHERE

IONOSPHERE

MESOSPHERE

········· OZONE LAYER

STRATOSPHERE

TROPOSPHERE

– our atmosphere would become swamped with carbon dioxide and eventually suffer the same fate as Venus – the death by heat of an uncontrolled greenhouse effect.

THE ATMOSPHERE

The Earth's atmosphere is unique in the Solar System, being composed of 78% nitrogen, 21% oxygen and only 1% of other elements. It extends several hundred miles above the surface of the planet but thins rapidly with increasing height. In fact, well over half the mass of the atmosphere is below the peak of Mount Everest.

The detailed structure and operation of the atmosphere is extremely complicated, as is well demonstrated by the problems encountered by forecasters when it comes to predicting the weather. For our purposes it is sufficient to consider the atmosphere as being composed of the layers shown in the diagram (*left*).

As the lowest level is the troposhere, where clouds, are formed. This is the area that contains most of the atmosphere's water vapour. It is in continuous motion and the combination of water vapour and turbulence is the cause of much annoyance to astronomers since it greatly disrupts the light from objects in space and hence reduces their visibility.

Above the troposphere is the stratosphere, the upper part of which is the much discussed "ozone" layer. As the name suggests, this is simply an area that contains a greater density of the element ozone. The importance of the ozone layer is that it reflects ultra-violet radiation from the Sun back into space. It is this ultra-violet radiation that, in small quantities, gives our skin a sun tan, but in large doses can cause skin cancer. Hence the concern over the depletion of ozone caused by certain chemical processes in our industrial environment.

The top part of the next layer, the mesosphere, and the layer above this, the thermosphere, contains a number of useful layers, collectively known as the ionosphere. This also reflects radiation, but reflects it back towards Earth. The radiation is in the form of radio waves, and it is the capability to reflect these that allows us to communicate by radio, even without help from artificial satellites.

It is in the lower regions of the ionosphere that we see the tiny particles often referred to as "shooting stars", or more correctly, meteors. These particles, often no bigger than grains of sand, are remnants left by travellers through the Solar System – comets, for example, that are drawn into the Earth's atmosphere and burn up, in much the same way as the heat shield on a space capsule burns as the ship re-enters the atmosphere.

The upper layer of the ionosphere, some 65 miles (100km) above Earth's surface, is sometimes lit up by the dancing displays of light known as aurorae. This is the result of the ionosphere being hit by energy-rich particles from the Sun that heat it: the light then emitted can look like a curtain across the sky.

MOON

IT IS NOT SURPRISING THAT THE MOON, as our closest neighbour in space, has received more attention that any other body in the night skies. Apart from being the most easily observable object, it also has a significant effect on our daily lives.

Even at a distance of less than 240,000 miles (385,000km) from Earth, the Moon exerts a very noticeable gravitational effect on us. This is most obviously demonstrated in the oceans where the "pull" of the Moon causes tides. The exact process by which the tides are caused is extremely complicated but the effect, combined with the gravitational attraction of the Sun, gives rise to the spring and neap tides when the Sun and Moon are in particular alignments.

One consequence of the force that the Moon exerts on the Earth is a kind of slingshot effect that causes the Moon to speed up slightly in its orbit, at which time the Earth's rotation slows down. As a result of this, the Moon is actually moving away from the Earth and our day is becoming longer. The effect is infinitesimally slow, but we can calculate that about 500 million years ago the Earth's day was only 22 hours long.

However, this does mean that one day the Moon will have an orbital period around the Earth that is exactly equal to the rotational period of Earth. The Moon will then be stationary above one point on the Earth's surface. At this time Earth's day will 55 times as long as it is now, but this won't happen for some billions of years.

Another familiar consequence of the Moon's motion around us is an eclipse of the Sun. This is the result of the Moon coming between the Earth and Sun, but it only happens on certain occasions because the orbit of the Moon is inclined at 5 degrees to the plane of the Earth's orbit around the Sun. If all three bodies moved in the same plane we would have an eclipse every month. Nevertheless, we do get a number of eclipses each year, but most are partial and, because 70 per cent of the Earth's surface is water, most occur over the oceans.

SURFACE OF THE MOON

We have seen that the Moon's gravitational pull on the Earth causes the tides in our oceans. The Earth has a similar effect on the Moon but, because there are no

ABOVE The surface of the far side of the Moon, never seen from Earth because the Moon rotates in exactly the time as it takes to orbit the Earth.

BELOW Astronaut James B Irwin with the Lunar Rover after their Apollo 15 Moon landing on July 31, 1971. This eerie picture shows Mount Hadley.

oceans there, this force acts on the body of the Moon itself; the Moon is not quite spherical and the Earth pulls at a bulge on the Moon's surface that has caused it to keep one side permanently pointing towards Earth. This means that we never see the "dark side" of the Moon. However, we seem to be lucky because orbiting spacecraft have shown that there is less to be seen on the other side.

The familiar pictures of the Moon's surface show that it has much in common with other rocky bodies in the Solar System. There is a general covering of craters that appear to have been caused by meteoric impacts, rather than volcanoes. These are more common in the highland areas and it is thought that the low-lying maria (from the Latin word for seas) were at one time just as heavily cratered, but that lava flows have covered the earliest of these.

A number of the maria are distinctly circular and these were probably very large impact craters that filled up with lava, almost to the rim of the crater.

One type of surface feature that has caused much speculation are the rilles. These have an appearence similar to river valleys and were thought to be evidence that running water had once existed on the Moon. They are, however, probably the result of the movement of geological faults and underground volcanic lava flows.

WHERE DID IT COME FROM?

A rather confusing result of analysing rock samples from the Apollo Moon landings is that the Moon appears to be older than the Earth. It has been suggested that this is because the Earth's surface has been changed by geological activity, and deep down the rocks are the same.

However, the relative quantities of certain elements are different in the case of Moon and Earth, which should not happen if both were formed from the same part of the initial cloud from which the Solar System condensed. One possibility is that the Moon formed in another part of the Solar System and somehow came to be wandering around, eventually to be caught in the Earth's gravitational field.

There is no generally accepted explanation for the problems raised by these inconsistencies and further exploration of the Moon will probably be required to solve the mystery.

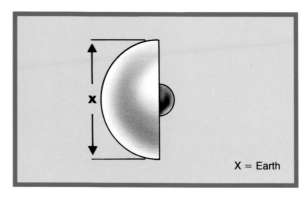

X = Earth

MARS

THE FOURTH PLANET OUT FROM THE SUN, Mars is the last of the terrestrial planets – the small, heavy worlds.

Further out there are only minor rocky bodies – the asteroids – and the Jovian planets – gas giants – after which we find the most distant of the known planets, Pluto. Beyond that icy world is the realm of the comets that visit us from the depths of the Solar System.

For many years Mars had a special attraction for astronomers. They believed its surface to show continents and oceans, canals and atmospheric clouds. An obvious next step was to suggest the presence of life on the planet, and this led to many popular stories and films about Martians and death-rays.

Today we know that the surface of Mars is nothing like this. Although it is almost 2500 miles (4000km) larger in diameter than Mercury, the surface gravity of the two planets is almost the same. This means that Mars can have only a very thin atmosphere, and the features observed by astronomers of old were probably nothing more than light and dark surface areas being covered and uncovered by dust storms; the continents, oceans and

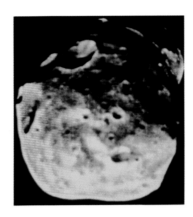

ABOVE Phobos, one of the two moons of Mars, is minute compared to our own Moon. Its small impact craters make it look rather like a potato.

BELOW The surface of Mars, taken by the Viking 1 lander, shows the reddish dust and rock covering that gives the planet its distinctive colour.

Physical Data		
distance from Sun	142 million miles (228Mkm)	
orbital period	687 days	
period of rotation	24 hours 37 minutes	
diameter	4,200 miles (6,790km)	
mass (Earth = 1)	0.11	
gravity (Earth = 1)	0.38	
temperature (degrees C)	−23	
moons:	diameter (miles)	distance from planet
Phobos	13.7 miles (22km)	5,800 miles (9,300km)
Deimos	7.5 miles (12km)	14,600 miles (23,500km)

X = Earth

canals were only the imaginings of over-enthusiastic and impressionable minds.

What we see from the numerous space probes that have visited the planet is very different. Mars has two polar ice caps, as does Earth, and these shrink and expand with the seasons. The rest of the surface shows characteristics that divide roughly equally between the northern and southern hemispheres; the north consists of low-lying flat plains, probably of volcanic origin, which show relatively recent craters only a few miles high; the south of high ground that shows heavy cratering, the craters being large and old.

There are extensive areas showing volcanic activity that has probably continued throughout Mars' history up to the present day, although no current activity is evident. Of the numerous volcanic craters on Mars one, Olympus Mons, is three times the height of Everest at 15.5 miles (25km), with a diameter of some 375 miles (600km).

But Mars has not always been as we see it now. When three Mariner spacecraft flew past the planet in the 1960s, there was nothing particularly exciting to report – just another dead, cratered world. Then, in 1971, Mariner 9 went into orbit around the planet. The photographs it sent back were a revelation. Apart from vast canyons and craters, there were winding valleys that could only have been carved by one thing – water!

So in its early history, Mars must have had a much denser and warmer atmosphere, probably high in carbon dioxide, which allowed surface water to exist. This carbon dioxide was absorbed and trapped in surface rocks, causing the atmospheric temperature to fall, as a result of which any free water would freeze into permafrost layers in the crust. With these key elements of its atmosphere either frozen or having escaped into space, Mars was left naked under the Sun. Deadly ultra-violet radiation poured down on the exposed surface, destroying any primitive life-forms that might by then have struggled into tenuous existence.

But with characteristic optimism, scientists sent more space probes in search of life – which almost certainly did not exist. Nevertheless, the thought was that it might be possible to detect the remains of ancient life. In 1976 two Viking spacecraft arrived in a Mars orbit, equipped with laboratories to detect organic material. Both soft-landed on the planet and began a series of experiments on the soil around them. Although there were some initially promising results the final conclusion was disappointing – no sign of life was apparent.

One minor but interesting point – why is Mars red? As we mentioned above, most of the planet's original water has been frozen into the surface soil; and this soil is rich in iron. And what is the result of a combination of water and iron? A rusty planet.

The Viking 1 spacecraft took this photograph as it approached Mars in 1976. Huge volcanoes can be seen on the planet's surface.

MINOR PLANETS/ ASTEROIDS

AS EARLY AS THE END OF THE 16th century, Johannes Kepler, developer of the three laws of planetary motion, noted that there was a very large gap between the orbits of Mars and Jupiter, and expressed his surprise that no planet existed there.

It was not until the latter part of the 18th century that the Titius-Bode law was published; it described the distances of planetary orbits from the Sun. This 'law' is a simple numerical sequence that predicts the position of the orbits accurately, but there appeared to be no planet matching the fifth number in the sequence, which fell between the orbits of Mars and Jupiter.

This was not widely accepted as proof of the existence of a missing planet, but when Uranus was discovered soon afterwards, and its orbit matched the next number in the Titius-Bode sequence, there was sudden interest in looking for the previously unknown body.

In 1801, an Italian astronomer, Piazzi, was compiling a star catalogue when he noticed a small object, which was in orbit around the Sun, moving against the background of stars. This orbit fitted the position of the missing planet as predicted by the Titius-Bode law. In fact, Piazzi had discovered the first of the asteroids – he named it Ceres, after the patron goddess of Sicily.

William Herschel first used the name asteroid, from the Latin meaning "star-like", but the terms "minor planet" and "planetoid" are also used to describe these objects.

By the end of the 19th century, more than three hundred of these small bodies had been identified, and today we believe that there may possibly be hundreds of thousands of them. Most of the minor planets move in a band of orbits, between the orbits of Mars and Jupiter, in what astronomers call to as the asteroid belt.

Other asteroids, known as the Trojan asteroids, travel in the same orbit as Jupiter and with the same orbital period. Yet more travel in elliptical orbits inside the asteroid belt and actually cross the Earth's orbit. These are known as the Apollo group, after the first of the type that were discovered, and may number as many as twenty individual objects.

WHAT IS AN ASTEROID?

During the formation of the Solar System the Sun condensed at the centre of the initial cloud of gas and dust, collecting the majority of the matter. Further out in the disk of the cloud, the planets began to form from small lumps, or planetesimals. In the area of greatest density the giant planets started to coalesce, the largest of these being Jupiter.

Between the orbits of Mars and Jupiter there were large numbers of planetesimals – sufficient to form a planet – but the massive gravitational field of Jupiter pulled at them, never allowing them to stick together to form a single body. The result is what we see today in the asteroid belt: a great swarm of minor planets.

The composition of the asteroids varies with their distance from the Sun. Out to just over two and a half times the distance between the Earth and Sun (this is roughly mid-way through the asteroid belt) most of the original ices have melted and been swept away, leaving

rocky planetoids. Further out than this the asteroids still contain ices and appear dark, just like the satellites of the outer planets.

CHIRON – ASTEROID OR COMET?

The most mysterious of the objects is Chiron. This is the most distant minor planet so far observed, having a very elliptical orbit that takes it from just inside the orbit of Saturn out almost as far as Uranus, more than twice as far again from the Sun.

But the mystery of Chiron lies not in its exceptional orbit but in its recent appearance. In the 1980s it began to brighten significantly. Some brightening had been expected, as the Chiron was in the part of its orbit that would bring it to its closest point to the Sun in 1996, but this alone would not account for the observations. Chiron seemed to be acting like a comet, possibly due to carbon dioxide ice turning to gas as it melted and ejecting dust to form a cloud around the asteroid.

Until very recently astronomers had made a firm distinction between the basically dark asteroids, made of solid materials, and comets, which were thought of as "dirty snowballs". Asteroids were considered to be inactive bodies, while comets appeared to release

considerable amounts of energy when they neared the Sun and began to melt, sometimes producing spectacular tails. But here was Chiron, an asteroid, breaking all the rules and showing traces of gas emissions that were previously associated only with comets.

One important point to note here is that when the Giotto spacecraft flew close to comet Halley in 1986, the comet's nucleus was much darker than expected, perhaps indicating that comets have a rocky or soil-like surface. This fact, combined with the observations of Chiron, has caused much discussion of the idea that there may not be as much difference between comets and asteroids as has always been thought.

If Chiron continues to behave as a comet, then this could have spectacular implications for the future. The asteroid will almost certainly have a close encounter with Saturn at some time and be thrown out of its current orbit. We don't know where it will go after this, but if it heads in towards Earth the results could be absolutely sensational. Comet Halley has given some dramatic displays in the past, with a nucleus about 9 miles (15km) across; Chiron has a diameter possibly as large as 155 miles (250km) – the largest comet ever seen.

a. JUPITER   d. SATURN
b. MARS   e. TROJAN ASTEROIDS
c. EARTH

The majority of the vast number of these minor planets are to be found in a belt between Mars and Jupiter. However, some are in two groups in Jupiter's orbit while others have elliptical orbits of their own.

JUPITER

THE FIRST OF THE JOVIAN PLANETS and the largest planet in the Solar System, Jupiter is one of the most exceptional objects in the skies; it is more massive than all other planets combined.

The majority of the planet consists of the light elements hydrogen and helium. Although it is referred to as a "gas giant", most of the gas has been so compressed by the temperatures and pressures inside the planet that it probably exists in a liquid state from just below the thin atmospheric layers at the surface. At the centre the core may be formed of iron silicates at temperatures of around 25,000 degrees or more.

Jupiter is a splendid object to study, even with binoculars. It is easy to see the four largest moons, and it was these that Galileo observed when first using a telescope – the fact that another planet had moons revolving around it was one of the nails in the coffin of

Physical Data

distance from Sun	483 million miles (778Mkm)
orbital period	11.9 years
period of rotation	9 hours 55.5 minutes
diameter	89,000 miles (143,000km)
mass (Earth = 1)	318
gravity (Earth = 1)	2.64
temperature (degrees C)	−150

moons: 16 known	diameter (miles)	distance from planet (000s miles)
Meltis	25 (40km)	80 (128km)
Adrastea	16 (40km)	80 (128km)
Amalthea	130 (210km)	112 (180km)
Thebe	62 (100km)	138 (222km)
Io	2,250 (3,630km)	262 (422km)
Europa	1,950 (3,138km)	417 (671km)
Ganymede	3,270 (5,262km)	665 (1,075km)
Callisto	2,980 (4,800km)	1,175 (1,880km)
Leda	6 (10km)	6,900 (11,100km)
Himalia	112 (180km)	7,135 (11,480km)
Lysithea	16 (25km)	7,285 (11,720km)
Elara	50 (80km)	7,295 (11,740km)
Ananke	16 (25km)	13,050 (21,000km)
Carme	19 (30km)	13,980 (22,500km)
Pasipae	25 (40km)	14,600 (23,500km)
Sinope	19 (30km)	14,700 (23,700km)

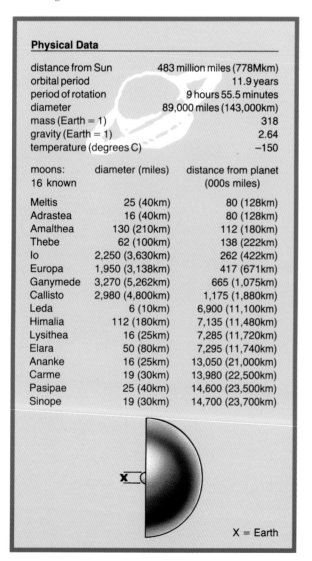

X = Earth

the Ptolemaic system, showing that the Earth was not the only centre of revolution in the universe.

With the help of a telescope, you can see the surface layers of the dense atmosphere. They appear as a series of bands or belts running around the planet, parallel to its equator. The white areas are giant clouds of rising gas, mainly consisting of ammonia. The darker areas are probably lower in the atmosphere, consisting of compounds of sulphur, and are warmer and descending.

The oval features, and particularly the famous Great Red Spot, are enormous storm systems – huge columns of rotating gas – that remain intact for long periods of time. The Great Red Spot has certainly been in existence for 300 years and possibly for much longer.

In the early days of the Solar System, Jupiter must have undergone the same processes as the Sun – the mass of gas that now forms the planet collapsed under its own gravitational field. As the ball of gas contracted, energy was generated and the core began to heat up. In the Sun the temperature eventually became sufficient for

hydrogen fusion to occur, but the internal temperature of Jupiter probably never reached more than 50,000 degrees. The planet still generates energy from gravitational contraction and so emits more energy than it receives from the Sun. Objects such as Jupiter, which generate energy but are not hot enough to shine as stars, are sometimes called brown dwarfs.

When the Voyager space probe travelled past Jupiter it made an unexpected discovery – the planet has rings. These are dark and extremely vague, which explains why they had not previously been seen from Earth. The rings stretch from out just above the clouds to some 87,000 miles (140,000km) above the planet.

Voyager also discovered a number of previously unknown moons around Jupiter. Even today we are not sure exactly how many there are in total. What is surprising is that the four largest moons, known as the Galilean satellites after the man who discovered them, are so different from one another.

Io, the closest of the four satellites to the planet, is covered with volcanoes. An object this small and so far from the Sun should have lost its original heat long ago, and it is thought that Io's continued activity is caused by gravitational effect of the other moons and Jupiter itself.

The next moon, Europa, is almost completely smooth, with only an occasional crater. The surface is covered with light and dark features, some running in straight lines, some in curves, but none of these seem to rise more than a few yards above the surface.

Ganymede is the largest moon of any planet. Its surface structure looks like a combination of both the Earth and the Moon, showing open plains, highlands, ridges and valleys, and areas of rugged mountains. The whole surface appears to be very old and possibly made up of both ice and rock.

The surface of Callisto is covered in craters but shows none of the rough features that occur on Ganymede. However, it is thought to be largely composed of ice.

ABOVE LEFT A Voyager 1 photograph of one of Jupiter's moons, Io. The enormous volcanic eruption, seen on the limb of the satellite, shows that objects far out in the universe can be very active.

LEFT Another Voyager 1 photograph shows the planet Jupiter with its satellite, Io, in front of the disk, and another, Europa, on the right against the blackness of space.

BELOW A Voyager 2 close-up of Jupiter's Great Red Spot, showing the enormous swirling cloud system. This vast storm has been seen from Earth for at least 200 years.

SATURN

WHEN GALILEO FIRST LOOKED AT SATURN through a
telescope he was baffled. His instrument was not of
sufficient quality to show the true nature of the rings. But
today we have glorious photographs from the Voyager
space probes that show details that cannot be seen even
when using the largest telescopes.

Undoubtedly Saturn is the most spectacular object in
the Solar System, but only recently have we understood
the complexity of its ring system. Through earthbound
telescopes we can see what appear to be three main rings,
but close passes by the Voyagers show that these are
actually made up of thousands of smaller rings, the gaps
between them being only changes in density of the overall
structure.

The rings are composed of material that was probably
left over after the initial formation of the main planet.
The particles that make up the rings vary in size from
microscopically small ones to others several yards across,
probably consisting of ice mixed with various elements
that produce the different colours.

Saturn and its rings are inclined at an angle to the plane
of the planet's motion around the Sun, just as the Earth is
inclined at 23.5 degrees in its orbit. This means that the
rings are sometimes edge-on to us, at which time they are
practically invisible. At other times they are "open", and
make a spectacular sight.

This effect caused Galileo even more problems. When
he had first seen Saturn, in 1610, the rings were open and
he interpreted what he saw as being a triple planet – he
thought that Saturn had two large moons in very close

RIGHT This Voyager 2 photograph of Saturn's rings shows their
extraordinarily elaborate structure.

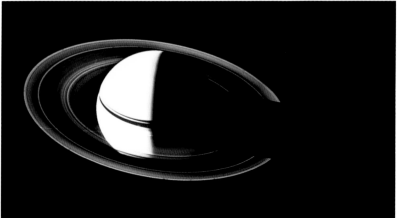

ABOVE Undoubtedly the most beautiful object in
the Solar System, Saturn is seen here from
Voyager 2 as it heads away from the planet.

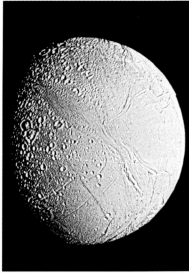

RIGHT Enceladus, one of Saturn's moons, has a
startling surface structure, with both craters and
valley-like features.

Physical Data

distance from the Sun	887 million miles (1,427Mkm)
orbital period	29.5 years
period of rotation	10 hours 40 minutes
diameter	74,568 miles (120,000km)
mass (Earth = 1)	95
gravity (Earth = 1)	1.16
temperature (degrees C)	−180

moons: 17+	diameter (miles)	distance from planet (000s miles)
Atlas	12.5 (20km)	85 (137km)
Prometheus	62 (100km)	86 (139km)
Pandora	56 (90km)	88 (142km)
Janus	124 (200km)	94 (151km)
Epimetheus	75 (120km)	94 (151km)
Mimas	242 (390km)	116 (186km)
Enceladus	317 (510km)	148 (238km)
Tethys	660 (1060km)	183 (295km)
Telesto	16 (25km)	183 (295km)
Calypso	16 (25km)	183 (295km)
Dione	695 (1120km)	234 (377km)
Helene	19 (30km)	234 (377km)
Rhea	950 (1530km)	328 (527km)
Titan	3,200 (5150km)	760 (1,222km)
Hyperion	155 (250km)	920 (1,481km)
Iapetus	900 (1460km)	2,213 (3,561km)
Phoebe	135 (220km)	8,050 (12,954km)

Other satellites have been observed by spacecraft but no further details are available.

X = Earth

orbit around it, which accounted for the planet's strange oval shape. But when he observed the planet a few years later, the rings were edge-on and his "moons" had disappeared. A few years later still, the rings were open and his "moons" were back.

The main body of the planet has a similar internal structure to that of Jupiter. The atmosphere shows the same type of features, including the oval-shaped storm systems, although there is nothing as permanent as the Great Red Spot. Also, both planets are rotating rapidly, giving them strong magnetic fields.

The numerous moons of Saturn are just as diverse as those of Jupiter. The largest, Titan, is one of the most extraordinary. Larger than Mercury, Titan has a dense atmosphere, composed largely of nitrogen – the main component of Earth's atmosphere. There is also some methane that may act in a similar way to water on Earth –

there may be methane rain, with methane oceans and methane snow. It is impossible to tell what the surface looks like, because of the density of the atmosphere.

The other large moons all have cratered surfaces, with some geological activity and a variety of valleys, as well as areas that appear to have been smoothed after the initial cratering – probably the result of the gravitational effects of other satellites. This is particularly evident on Enceladus, shown in the photograph (*near left*).

The smaller moons hold just as many surprises. On either side of one of Saturn's outer rings two small satellites travel in unison – as if shepherding the particles of the ring into a tight band. Two others travel in another very close orbit, every four years, they get close enough together so that their mutual gravitational attraction causes them to perform a dance, during which they change places, the leader becoming the follower.

URANUS

FOR ALL RECORDED HISTORY astronomers believed that there were six planets, Saturn being the outermost. That was until 1781, when William Herschel made a notable and unexpected discovery.

He was an enthusiastic amateur astronomer and spent every available moment studying the stars. As with many discoveries in astronomy, the observer was looking for something other than what was found and Herschel was trying to find stars that appeared close together, in the line of sight. He reasoned that it would be possible to calculate the distance to a star, by the method we now call trigonometric parallax, if he could find two such stars.

On 13 March 1781 he looked at a "star" that did not appear as a point, as all other stars do, but got bigger as he increased the magnification. He thought he had discovered a comet. It never occurred to him that he had found a new planet – nobody had done that for thousands of years. Over the next few days he noted that the object moved against the background of stars. He still believed it to be a comet, but astronomers studied its motion and found that it was not travelling in the orbit known to be characteristic of such a body. There was no doubt – Herschel had found the seventh planet.

Of the four Jovian planets – the gas giants – Uranus stands out in a number of ways. Unlike the others it generates practically no energy of its own. No one knows

Titania, the largest satellite of Uranus, is yet another moon that has a complicated surface structure.

The almost featureless blue of the planet Uranus is characteristic of the dense methane atmosphere.

why. This results in the surprising fact that the surface temperature on Uranus is about the same as that on Neptune, despite the latter being around half as far again from the Sun.

Another difference is in the planet's appearance; there are no visible features in the atmosphere of Uranus, while the others all show belts and storms. Nevertheless, Uranus is spectacular for just this reason: it is a giant world of mystery, bathed in an almost ghostly blue light.

It is now believed that the structure of the planet is somewhat different to that of Jupiter and Saturn. The core is cold and composed of rock, and about the size of the Earth. Above this is a vast mantle of liquid water, methane and ammonia, comprising about two-thirds of

Physical Data

distance from Sun	1,780 million miles (2,870Mkm)
orbital period	84 years
period of rotation	16 hours
diameter	32,560 miles (52,400km)
mass (Earth = 1)	15
gravity (Earth = 1)	1.11
temperature (degrees C)	−210

moons:	diameter (miles)	distance from planet (000s miles)
Miranda	300 (485km)	81 (130km)
Ariel	720 (1,160km)	119 (192km)
Umbriel	740 (1,190km)	166 (267km)
Titania	1,000 (1,610km)	272 (438km)
Oberon	960 (1,550km)	364 (586km)

Ten additional satellites were discovered by Voyager 2 in 1986, but these are small and dark and little is known of them. All of them are within the orbit of Miranda.

X

X = Earth

the mass of the planet. At the surface are atmospheric layers of hydrogen and helium.

One feature of Uranus is unique in the Solar System – the axis of the planet is tilted at 98 degrees to the plane of its orbit. This means that the planet and its moons appear to be going round the Sun on their side. What caused this extraordinary inclination is a mystery.

In 1977 it was discovered that Uranus has a system of thin rings. These rings, and the 10 smaller satellites, are all composed of icy material (organic, in terms of chemistry, at the surface), which becomes very dark when exposed to ultraviolet light. This type of material is common in the outer reaches of the Solar System and is probably the same material from which comets are formed. The particularly dark nature of these bodies explains why they have not been spotted by astronomers until recently.

Although Miranda is the smallest of the five large moons, it has interesting features. The surface shows many densely cratered areas, but there are also regions where the crust is mottled. Planetary geologists think that the satellite may have been blown apart and reassembled, possibly several times. This is hard to explain because the icy substances, of which all the satellites are composed, are thought to be extremly solid and we cannot predict their behaviour in such violent circumstances.

NEPTUNE

AFTER THE DISCOVERY OF URANUS, astronomers calculated its orbit. This had been done successfully for other planets and there was no reason why there should be any difference in the case of Uranus. But when observations had been made, the planet did not follow the path that had been predicted.

This gave rise to much speculation that there was an eighth planet beyond Uranus. The gravitational pull of such a planet would cause disturbances in the orbit of Uranus that could explain the discrepancies between predictions and observations. This was all very well in theory, but how do you find a missing planet? It might be hundreds of years before somebody found it by accident, as Herschel had found Uranus, and trying to calculate where it should be found was a horrifying task in the days before computers.

Nevertheless, two young astronomers, John Couch Adams in England and Leverrier in France, wrestled independently with the problem in the early 19th century. After two years of work both had the answer. Adams was first to finish, though the establishment didn't take him seriously. A search was begun but, due to general incompetence, the chance to discover the eighth planet was lost. Leverrier, however, was more successful - he sent his calculations to Berlin Observatory, which set to work and found the new planet.

Because of its great distance from the Sun, very little was known of Neptune and its moons until the 1980s. Astronomers had observed cloud systems in the planet's atmosphere and seen the two moons, Triton and Nereid. There was speculation about a ring system but observations suggested that this must be very strange indeed – a set of arcs around the planet rather than continuous rings.

In 1989, Voyager 2 flew past Neptune and provided answers as well as posing more questions. The planet's atmosphere is similar to that of Uranus but shows a degree of detail that was unexpected. The Great Dark Spot, for example, looks much like the Red Spot of Jupiter; it is a vast anticyclone – a high pressure storm – which changes its size and shape in a matter of days. There are a number of other storm systems, some traversing the planet at great speed. What drives these systems is still a mystery.

The internal structures of Uranus and Neptune are thought to be much the same, but the core of Neptune is generating heat – at least 40% of the heat given out comes from the core. What is strange is that the temperatures of the two planets' atmospheres are very much the same. Also, the variation of temperature with latitude on the planets' surface is odd. We all know that the Earth's equator is very much hotter than the frozen poles, but on

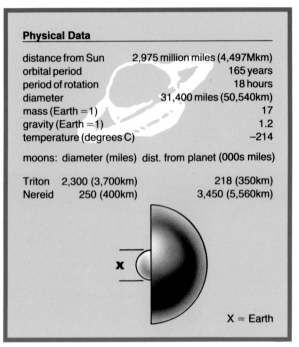

Physical Data

distance from Sun	2,975 million miles (4,497Mkm)
orbital period	165 years
period of rotation	18 hours
diameter	31,400 miles (50,540km)
mass (Earth =1)	17
gravity (Earth =1)	1.2
temperature (degrees C)	−214

moons:	diameter (miles)	dist. from planet (000s miles)
Triton	2,300 (3,700km)	218 (350km)
Nereid	250 (400km)	3,450 (5,560km)

X = Earth

Uranus and Neptune the coolest areas are the mid-northern and -southern latitudes, and these are only a few degrees lower in temperature than the rest of the planet.

As was predicted, Neptune has a system of rings and they are indeed partial rings or arcs. This is yet another mystery, because the particles that make up these "ring arcs" should bump into each other and spread themselves out into a continuous ring in only a few years.

The moons of Neptune provide us with yet more novelties. Nereid, the smallest of the two satellites that had been seen from Earth, has a most eccentric orbit – at its furthest from the planet it is seven times more distant than at its closest approach. Triton, by far the largest of the moons, is another unusual object: it is the only major moon to go around its planet in the opposite direction to the planet's rotation. Also, it has a thin atmosphere of nitrogen that comes from gas given off from the polar cap and from geysers caused by volcanic activity. The surface of Triton shows a wide range of features from open plains to large craters and a strange furrowed region looking like a giant road network.

The Voyager 2 spacecraft discovered 6 further moons, the largest being bigger than Nereid, but this could not be seen from Earth because its orbit is so close to the planet that it is hidden by the glare.

Neptune is the last of the worlds to be visited by Voyager 2 and it may be a long time before any other spacecraft venture into the depths of the Solar System, but the information gained so far will keep scientists busy, and confused, for many years to come.

ABOVE Neptune, the twin planet of Uranus, has a similar blue methane atmosphere but giant storm clouds as well.

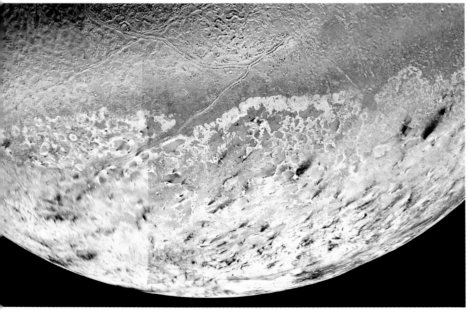

LEFT Triton, Neptune's largest moon, is another satellite that has a great variety of surface features, including polar caps, plains and valleys, as seen in this composite photograph.

PLUTO

THE NINTH PLANET OUT from the Sun and the last of those currently known, Pluto is also the smallest of the planets, being tinier even than Earth's Moon. Pluto is peculiar in the Solar System in that it is unlike either the four inner terrestrial planets or the giant Jovian planets. It is thought to be an icy body, similar to some of the moons of the other outer planets, covered with a layer of methane frost.

Because Pluto is so small and distant it is difficult to obtain information about it with any degree of certainty. The most noticable fact – and one of the few in which we can have confidence – is that its orbit is the most unusual of any planet. Although Pluto is generally regarded to be the furthest planet from the Sun, this is not always correct – the eccentricity of Pluto's orbit is so great that the planet sometimes moves inside the orbit of Neptune, as is the case in the years between 1979 and 1999. Another unusual facet of the orbit is that it is inclined to the plane in which the other planets' orbits lie at an angle of 118 degrees, and goes around the Sun in the opposite direction to the others.

The search for Pluto followed much the same lines as the search for Neptune. Observers realised that the errors in the prediction of Uranus' orbit were due to something other than the presence of Neptune alone. Various astronomers made calculations of where Pluto should be found, and indeed some of them actually took photographs of it. Unfortunately for them, they thought that the new planet was much larger than it actually is and so never spotted it in their pictures. The discovery of Pluto was made early in 1930 by an American amateur astronomer who had been temporarily employed by the Lowell observatory to check photographs of the sky in the hopes of finding the planet. His name was Clyde Tombaugh, and he became only the third person in recorded history to have actually discovered a previously unknown planet.

Having found the new planet, astronomers were keen to demonstrate that it did indeed account for the effect on the orbits of Uranus and Neptune which had led to the prediction of its position. However, Pluto was far smaller than anticipated and could not possibly have sufficient mass to disturb the two gas giants. Being so small and distant, Pluto was no more than a star-like image in even the largest telescopes, and so the mystery continued for almost 50 years.

Then, in 1978, a researcher, called Jim Christy, was studying some photographic plates to check the exact position of stars and planets. He was looking specifically at the position of Pluto, when he noticed that the image of the planet appeared to be blurred into a pear shape. After checking other pictures of Pluto it became obvious that this blurring had occurred before, and that it was not just a fault on the plates. There was only one conclusion: Pluto had a large moon orbiting close by.

This moon was named Charon and, together with its parent planet, accounted for some of the missing mass that was needed to explain the disturbances in the orbits of Uranus and Neptune. One peculiar feature of Charon is that its orbital period around Pluto is exactly the same as the period of rotation of the planet, so Charon always stays in the same position in Pluto's sky.

But still there was some speculation that a tenth planet existed and various searches were carried out, though to no avail. The difficulty was that the positions of the outer planets had not been plotted for a sufficiently long period to allow precise calculations to be made of where such a tenth planet would be.

However, today we have the ideal means to provide us with exact positions and detailed information about gravitational disturbances: the four spacecraft, Pioneer 10 and 11 and Voyager 1 and 2. As these travel out of the Solar System they will be tracked; any variation noticed from their expected position might be caused by the gravitational pull of a tenth planet. Examination of these variations should allow us to predict the position of this planet and, it is hoped, we should then be able to find it in the deep sky photographs that already exist.

ABOVE These two photographs show Pluto and its moon, Charon. The one on the left is from one of the best ground-based telescopes; the one on the right was taken from Earth's orbit by the Hubble Space Telescope.

RIGHT The ancient view of the Solar System, as in *Harmonia Macrocosmica,* by Cellarius in 1660, did not include Uranus, Neptune or Pluto.

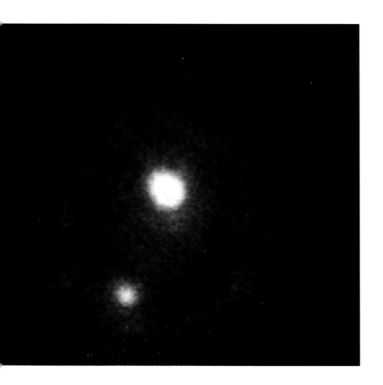

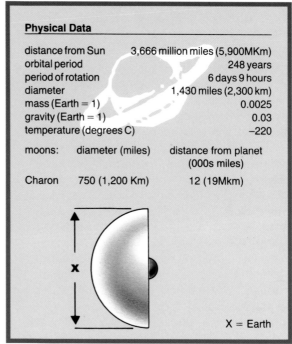

Physical Data

distance from Sun	3,666 million miles (5,900MKm)
orbital period	248 years
period of rotation	6 days 9 hours
diameter	1,430 miles (2,300 km)
mass (Earth = 1)	0.0025
gravity (Earth = 1)	0.03
temperature (degrees C)	−220

moons:	diameter (miles)	distance from planet (000s miles)
Charon	750 (1,200 Km)	12 (19Mkm)

X = Earth

COMETS

OCCASIONAL VISITORS TO THE INNER PLANETS, the comets have been appearing in our skies since the birth of the Solar System. Most are too small and faint to be noticed by people who are not looking for them specifically, but the rare examples that are seen give rise to some of the most spectacular events we can hope to see with the naked eye. They also offer us a chance to understand more about our own origins, for the matter of which comets are made up could possibly date back to the birth of the Sun and the planets. Perhaps this was sensed by the astronomers and soothsayers of the past, who regarded the appearance of a comet as an omen – either for good or ill. Halley's comet, for example, has both thrilled and scared observers on Earth for centuries.

Comets are what was left behind after the formation of the gas giants that inhabit the cold outer reaches of the Solar System. Here the heat of the Sun was insufficient to melt the ice of planetesimals, the building blocks of the planets. Lumps of rock and ice that were not swallowed up in this planet-forming phase were pulled outwards by the gravitational forces of the giant planets, and thrown into distant orbits, thousands of times further from the Sun than Earth.

This debris forms a vast disk of material stretching outward, some of the planetesimals spreading out away from the disk and eventually forming an enormous sphere around the Solar System. This sphere could contain billions of individual objects, the furthest of them possibly two light years distant – half way to the next star system. Its sphere is now called the Oort Cloud (after Jan Hendrik Oort, the Dutch astronomer who suggested its existence in 1950) and it is from here that comets begin their long and lonely journey towards the heat of the realm occupied by the inner planets.

But they don't just have to fall out of the Oort Cloud of their own accord. They have to be disturbed from their remote orbits, where they have waited for billions of years.

The stars are not as fixed in space as we might think from the way they appear to stay in the same position in the skies. Over astronomical time scales they move about in relation to each other, and in the lifetime of the Solar System it is probable that thousands of stars have passed relatively close by. The gravitational pull of such stars would disturb comets in the Oort Cloud, sending some into new orbits which take them near to the Sun.

Some of these orbits will cause some comets to travel past the Sun and out of the Solar System forever, but others will be trapped in the gravitational fields of the Sun and planets and remain in elliptical orbits, returning time and time again. The period between one visit of an individual comet and the next may be as short as a few years or as long as millions of years.

HEADS AND TAILS

As comets journey towards the Sun, the frozen material of which they are composed begins to melt. This causes jets of gas and dust to be ejected from the surface and form a cloud around the nucleus – the main body of the comet. This cloud is called the head, or "coma", of the comet. As the comet comes closer and closer to the Sun, more ices melt and the coma expands. It is this matter that forms the comet's tail.

It is natural to think that the tail is being swept back behind the comet as it rushes through space, but there is no atmosphere to create this effect. In fact, the tail is being swept away from the comet, but not always behind it. The diagram on the right shows the tail as the comet travels around Sun. You can see that it always points away from the Sun, and that the tail is actually in front of the comet's head as it travels away from the Sun on its journey back out into the Solar System.

It seems as if the tail is being pushed away from the Sun, and this is exactly what is happening. The Sun is constantly giving off both radiation, which we see as light, and streams of very small charged particles, known as the Solar Wind. The first of these, the sunlight, is the cause of the most prominent part of the comet's tail.

As dust is ejected by jets of gas from the nucleus of the comet, the sunlight actually exerts a very slight pressure on that dust. These particles are so small that the pressure is sufficient to sweep them away from the coma and form the glorious curving tail. The reason that the

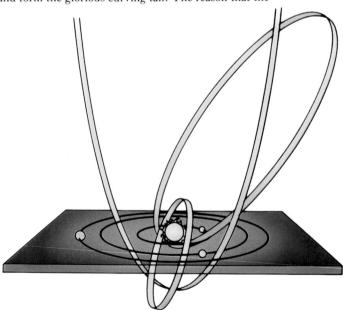

Comets originating from the Oort Cloud may sweep through the Solar System in any of a number of different orbits, not necessarily in the plane of the planets.

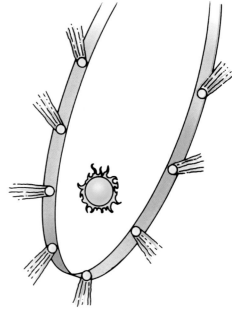

TOP As a comet moves in its orbit, its tails always point away from the Sun.

ABOVE The tail may have two components, one of dust (curved) and one of charged particles (straight).

LEFT The spectacular Comet West of 1976, showing its various tails as it is swept out away from the Sun.

tail is curved is because each of the dust particles is actually orbiting the Sun, but in very slightly different orbits. The particles that are further from the Sun, albeit by a very small amount, travel more slowly than those that are closer. The faster particles overtake the slower ones, and this is what gives the tail its characteristic curve. In fact, this part of the tail is known as the "dust tail", because of its composition.

There is a second component to the tail, caused by the Solar Wind. During the process that creates the dust tail, some of the particles in the coma are affected by a wave of light which causes them to break up into small particles that may carry electric charges. As the Solar Wind sweeps past the head of the comet, it interacts with these charged particles and causes them to form the second part of the tail, but this time it is a straight tail, pointing directly

away from the Sun. The charged particles that form this type of tail are called ions, and consequently this part is called the ion tail.

When a comet is seen in the sky it rarely appears to be very large, and most examples are never seen by the casual observer. The actual size is largely related to the initial size of the nucleus, and the size of the coma and tail are determined by how close the comet comes to the Sun (i.e. how much ice has melted). The apparent size is obviously affected by how close the comet comes to the Earth as it crosses our orbit. But even when comets that stretch across the entire sky are seen, it is difficult to appreciate just how big they actually are: great comets of the past have been seen with comas around the nucleus that have diameters of some 1.25 million miles (2Mkm), and tails hundreds of millions of miles long.

THE MILKY WAY — OUR GALAXY

IF YOU LOOK AT THE NIGHT SKY you will see thousands of points of light. Most of these are stars, just like our Sun; a few of the lights are planets, which look much like stars, though some are a little brighter.

But as you look at these bright points, even with the naked eye, a pattern will start to emerge. Sweeping across the sky, from one horizon to the other, is a broad band of light, rather like a glowing pathway through the stars. Ancient civilisations named this the Milky Way.

If you count the number of stars you can see just with the naked eye you will find there are about three thousand. But if you first use binoculars, and then a small telescope, then a moderate sized telescope, and finally the huge instruments that sit on mountain tops in remote locations, you will see ever more stars, almost without end. If you were to point such an instrument at the Milky Way, you would see that it is not in fact continuous, but an area of sky filled with such numbers of stars, millions upon millions of them, that there appears to be no space between them. .

When you look at the sky through a telescope you will see

An artist's impression of our Galaxy shown both edge-on (top) and as it would appear when seen from above, displaying the spiral structure. The red circle roughly indicates the Sun's position.

objects that do not look like stars but hazy patches. Some of these are bright clouds of gas and dust, just like the one that was the birth place of our own Solar System, in which other stars are forming – these may have their own family of planets one day. Such clouds can be seen all over the sky, and come in all shapes and sizes, but are all part of our galaxy. They are the nebulae: great clouds that are among the most spectacular of all the wonders of the universe.

EVEN MORE STARS

There are other objects, out in the depths of space, that are similar to the nebulae, but are regular in shape: round, oval or cigar-shaped. If you look more closely you will begin to see some structure – like catherine-wheels, or whirlpools. An even closer look shows that these objects are much the same as the band of light we call the Milky Way – a gentle glow that consists of millions of individual stars. In fact, these are other galaxies, unbelievably far away, outside our own galaxy.

So, at last, we can get some idea of the shape of our own galaxy. It seems reasonable to assume that the Milky Way is similar to the other galaxies we see in space. This is just as well, because we have no chance of travelling outside our own galaxy to take a photograph: even the closest stars would take more than four years to reach if we were travelling at the speed of light, and there seems little likelihood of us reaching even a fraction of this speed with our current technology. The edge of our galaxy would take as much as twenty thousand years to reach at light speed.

As we cannot currently hope to take a photograph of the Milky Way from outside we have used an artist's impression to show our understanding of its structure. This is quite reasonable, because many other galaxies have the same shape, and our observations from inside agree with what we would expect to see if the galaxy is indeed a vast catherine wheel.

But we can see that other galaxies have different shapes, so how do we decide which one is right for the Milky Way? What if all the other galaxies are roughly the same shape and they look different because of the angle from which we see them? If a galaxy is shaped like a thick pizza then it would look round when viewed from above or below; cigar-shaped if viewed edge-on; and oval from any angle in between. In fact, our galaxy looks more like two fried eggs, back to back, because it has a central bulge that is called the nucleus.

And what about the catherine-wheel shape? Well, galaxies are made up of millions of stars and the spiral

A spiral galaxy, similar to our own, seen edge-on and showing the plane of the galaxy and the central bulge of the nucleus.

arms are massive aggregations of these stars sweeping out from the nucleus, separated by vast gulfs of empty space, thousands of light years across.

OUR PLACE IN THE GALAXY

Now we know the general shape and structure of our galaxy it is useful to look at some more precise details of its make-up and where we fit in to the galaxy as a whole.

Because of its shape we refer to the Milky Way as a spiral galaxy. In fact it is a giant spiral and one of the largest galaxies – it contains at least 100,000 million stars and has a diameter, from one edge of the spiral disk to the other, of about 100,000 light years.

Our Sun holds no special position in the galaxy and we are about two-thirds of the way from the galactic nucleus out towards the edge, in one of the spiral arms.

THE ORIGIN OF OUR GALAXY

In the same way that the Sun formed from a cloud of interstellar gas and dust, our galaxy is thought to have had its origins in a vast gas cloud comprised mainly of hydrogen with some helium. This cloud is referred to as a protogalaxy, and was probably several hundreds of thousands of light years in diameter.

The mutual gravitational attraction of the matter in the cloud caused it to begin contracting about 15,000 million years ago, soon after the universe was born (more about the origins of the universe in Section 3, *pp 128-9*). Star formation began in the centre of the cloud, where the density was greatest, and the stars born here formed the early galactic nucleus.

Throughout the cloud there were some local areas in which density was greater than average, and in these regions great clusters of stars formed. These were the globular clusters, and they occupied a vast sphere around the nucleus of the galaxy. As the original cloud continued to contract towards the nucleus and disk, these clusters remained in place to form the "halo" of globular clusters we see today.

The processes that caused the initial cloud, and hence the galaxy, to begin rotating are not well understood, but the rotation increased as the cloud shrank and caused the majority of the matter to be concentrated in the disk we see today.

Many of the earliest stars have evolved to the end of their lives and have exploded, giving up their matter for the formation of newer stars. But some of the gas from the original cloud still remains and the regions in which it is found are occasionally compressed by the explosion of older stars, to trigger the birth of yet more stars.

STARS IN OUR GALAXY

THE SUN WAS FORMED from a cloud of gas, mainly consisting of hydrogen, that contracted and eventually became hot enough for a nuclear reaction to occur in which the hydrogen was converted into helium, giving off energy in the process. As described on page 24, when most of the hydrogen is used up the helium will begin to be converted, or fused, and further energy will be given out. Conversion of other elements may occur when most of the helium has been converted, but these processes add little to the life of a star.

Exactly what is going on inside the star is extremely complicated, but for now it is only important to realise that the star is using up its fuel – hydrogen, helium, and so on – and giving out energy in the process. Eventually the star will exhaust all the available fuel and die.

All stars form from clouds of gas and dust, just like the way in which the Sun was born. However, the size of initial clouds can be very different, giving a variable initial mass – and this has an important effect on its subsequent evolution. It is natural to think that stars that contain the most matter will survive for the longest time, but, in fact, the reverse is actually true. Stars like the Sun may take 10,000 million years to 'burn' all their hydrogen fuel, but stars with as much as 20 times the mass of the Sun will use up their hydrogen in as little as one million years. An analogy for this is a large bonfire that uses up all its fuel in a matter of minutes, while a gently burning log fire may last for hours.

There is an enormous variation in the size, mass, temperature, and so on, of different stars, and there are a number of ways of classifying them. The major groups are: supergiant, bright giant, giant, sub-giant, dwarf, sub-dwarf and white dwarf.

The biggest, the supergiants, have incredible mass – they can be as large as 1000 times the diameter of the Sun – but they may have relatively low surface temperatures of only a few thousand degrees. At the other end of the scale, a white dwarf may have a diameter only one per cent of the Sun's, but may be thousands of degrees hotter in temperature.

If a graph of the luminosity of a star (the total amount of light it gives out) is plotted against its surface temperature (which also determines its colour) the result is a diagram that shows a great deal about the way stars evolve. It is known as the Hertzsprung-Russell diagram (abbreviated to "H-R diagram") after the two astronomers who first published it in 1913.

This shows that the distribution of stars is not random, and that there is an obvious belt, running from the top left to the bottom right. This belt is called the main sequence, and the majority of all stars appear on it. There is also a less well defined area, from just above centre towards the upper right, called the giant branch.

TOP A view towards the centre of the Milky Way, showing the region of the constellation Sagittarius, bright with millions of stars and nebulae and intersected by dust lanes.

BOTTOM Star clouds in the constellations of Scutum and Sagittarius, near the centre of the Milky Way.

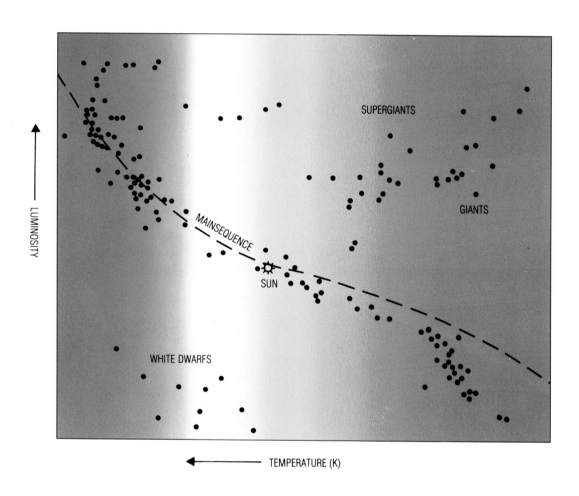

LUMINOSITY

SUPERGIANTS

MAINSEQUENCE

SUN

GIANTS

WHITE DWARFS

TEMPERATURE (K)

Stars are not scattered randomly on the H-R diagram. The majority appear on the main sequence, soon after they form, when equilibrium is reached, evolving later onto the giant branch and finally becoming white dwarfs.

Stars appear in different positions on the H-R diagram according to their initial mass and their age. If the position of a star of a particular mass is plotted at different ages we can see the way in which that star evolves during its life.

When a star first forms from a cloud of gas, and starts to generate energy by hydrogen fusion, it appears on the main sequence of the H-R diagram. If it is an average star, like the Sun, it joins the main sequence roughly in the middle and stays there for thousands of millions of years. If it has much more mass, say 15 times the mass of the Sun, it joins at the top left and stays there for only a few million years. The time a star spends on the main sequence is the length of time it takes to use up its

hydrogen fuel. As the hydrogen starts to run out, the star make a few internal changes and moves to the giant branch of the H-R diagram, its exact position being determined by its mass. From the giant stage the star changes relatively rapidly; sometimes it becomes unstable, blowing off outer layers of its atmosphere, and eventually turns into a white dwarf, appearing on the bottom left of the Hertzsprung-Russell diagram.

The important factor in the star's evolution is its initial mass, and particularly large stars may end up in a cataclysmic explosion called a supernova, in which most or all of the star is destroyed. If, however, there is anything left of the core of the star, it will either collapse into a neutron star – an object that has the mass of the Sun but has been squeezed by its own gravity so that it is only a few miles across – or, for very massive stars, collapse completely to form a black hole. We shall look at these exotic objects in more detail in Section 3 (*pp 124-5*).

NEBULAE/STAR CLUSTERS

AMID THE STARS, which are so prominent in the night sky, are numerous hazy patches. These are named nebulae, from the Latin word meaning mist – the term describes them well, because they look like faintly luminous clouds on a dark night. A number of nebulae can be seen with the naked eye, but a long-exposure photograph is necessary to obtain a good view.

For many years it was thought that all these hazy patches were clouds of gas, but we now know that there are a number of distinctly different types of nebulae. There is a very important distinction between those that are actually composed of gas and lie within our galaxy, and those that look like hazy clouds but are really remote galaxies of stars, looking as they do because of their enormous distance from us.

For the moment, though, we are only interested in the gaseous clouds that are part of the Milky Way – the various different types are described overleaf. It is important to remember that all nebulae are composed of gas, mainly hydrogen, and dust particles. The hydrogen is generally that left over from the formation of the galaxy, and the heavier elements were created in ancient stars and released when they exploded.

ABOVE A planetary nebula is a shell of expanding gas that has been ejected from a dying star.

These two emission nebulae, Omega BELOW and the Tarantula RIGHT, are giant clouds of gas and dust heated by radiation from stars within them.

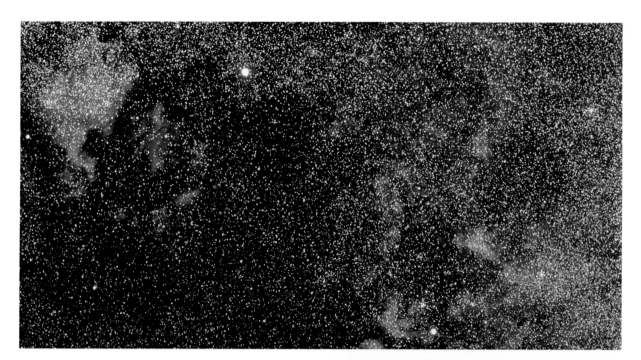

TOP Nebula-rich region of the Milky Way in the constellation Cygnus. The North America Nebula can be seen top left, and to its right is the small Pelican Nebula.

RIGHT Part of the Milky Way, with red emission nebulae and a double globular cluster in the constellation of Perseus.

EMISSION NEBULAE

These are clouds consisting mainly of hydrogen that have stars embedded in them – they shine because the stars heat the gas. The gas absorbs the starlight and emits it with the characteristic colour of the gas – in the case of hydrogen this is red.

Emission nebulae can be several tens of light years in diameter, and contain enough material to form many stars, and indeed we often see very young stars that have recently formed inside them.

REFLECTION NEBULAE

This type of nebula contains gas, but shines not because the gas is hot but because there are dust particles in the cloud. Light from nearby stars is reflected from this dust, hence the name, and so has the colour of the star from which the original light came, rather than that characteristic of the gas.

Generally, reflection nebulae are seen near young hot blue stars, so they appear blue. Sometimes, though, emission nebulae are found in the same region of space as reflection nebulae.

ABSORPTION NEBULAE

These are clouds of cold dark gas and dust. Normally, they would not be seen, but they can be detected because they lie between us and more distant stars, obscuring their light. In areas where there are dense star fields absorption nebulae show up as dark areas against the stellar background.

Large areas of the sky can be obscured by such nebulae, which often appear as huge streaks. These are usually referred to as "dust lanes", and can sometimes be seen in far distant galaxies.

PLANETARY NEBULAE

In the 19th century, when optical telescopes were far less sophisticated than they are today, these objects appeared as small bright disks, just like planets. Without knowing their true nature, the astronomers of those days named them "planetary" nebulae.

Today we know that this type of nebula is caused by the explosive ejection of a star's atmosphere into space, during the dying stages of its life. The result is a shell of gas that expands into space, away from the star. The gas is heated by the central star, which has become a white dwarf – this type of star is extremely hot and emits ultra-violet light that is absorbed and then emitted by the gas of the nebula. During its life the star will have created some oxygen in its core and this can be detected in the nebula by the characteristic green colouration of the light that it emits.

There must have been many stars in the history of the Galaxy that underwent the process of ejecting such planetary nebulae, but as they expand these nebulae become diffuse and, after perhaps 100,000 years, are too faint to be seen. The result is that we see relatively few of these objects today.

ABOVE and RIGHT These two objects are both globular clusters, several thousand light years away and containing hundreds of thousands of stars.

OPEN CLUSTERS

Also known as "galactic" clusters, because they all occur in the main disk of the Galaxy, these groups of stars are generally relatively young. Typically containing a few hundred stars, open clusters are more loosely bound by gravity than globular clusters and so tend to split up into individual stars on time scale in the order of hundreds of millions of years, although a few are much older.

Open clusters are not as spectacular as globular clusters but have their own points of special interest. At great distances they are indistinguishable from background stars, so the ones we see are relatively close – no more than a few thousand light years away. The stars in any open cluster all formed at about the same, from the same cloud of interstellar gas, and being young they give us the opportunity to study the evolution of infant stars. In fact, many open clusters are so young that it is still possible to see the remnants of the gas cloud from which they originally formed.

GLOBULAR CLUSTERS

These objects are among the most beautiful sights in the sky. They consist of anything from 10,000 to 1 million stars linked together by gravity to form a densely packed sphere, typically of around 100 light years in diameter. We know of about 200 globular clusters, spread in a giant sphere or halo around the galactic disk.

The stars in these clusters are some of the oldest in the Galaxy, having formed more than 10,000 million years ago. As a result, they are far advanced on the evolutionary path and consist mainly of red giants, with some red and white dwarfs.

Some of these stars are of a type known as Cepheid variables, which vary in brightness over a regular period. The length of this period is related to the actual brightness of the star. If we know how bright the star really is, and we check how bright it appears to be, we can calculate how far away it is. So, by observing Cepheid variables in globular clusters, which can be seen all over the sky, we make an estimate of how big the Galaxy is.

THE MILKY WAY AND BEYOND

SO FAR WE HAVE LOOKED NO FURTHER than those small corners of space with which we feel intimately associated; the Solar System, with our own Sun and planets, is so tiny that it goes unnoticed by all but our closest neighbours; our own galaxy, the Milky Way, which fills the sky with its stars and nebulae is, for all its enormous bulk, less than a pinpoint against the seemingly infinite reaches of the unimaginably huge universe.

Beyond the stars of the Milky Way there is an immense gulf. For a distance greater than the length of our entire Galaxy there is nothing but emptiness. But the sky is not completely black. Some faint misty patches inhabit the darkness. These objects are not just clouds of gas, like the beautiful nebulae that shine red, green and blue, well within our own system of stars, but are star systems. However, they are so distant that they have gone all but unseen – until recently.

THE LOCAL GROUP

As we travel further from the comforting blaze of the 100 billion suns that makes up our spiral home, we can see two of the faintly glowing star clouds that are other galaxies, almost 200,000 light years away. These are the Large and Small Magellanic clouds, named after the famous explorer who first reported them. Smaller than our own Milky Way, these dwarf galaxies, companions to our own, orbit like satellites, each of them containing several billion stars.

Looking around us we can see more of these dwarf galaxies, at least 10 within a million light years; there are probably many more. But as we move out into space there is another mighty galaxy – no dwarf this, but a spiral giant like our own. This is the Andromeda galaxy, over two million light years away and 180,000 light years across, with twice the mass of the Milky Way. It has its own attendant dwarf galaxies and together the two giant spirals and their satellites makes up the local group of galaxies.

SUPERCLUSTERS

If we were at a point 10 million light years from home, we might just be able to see the two major galaxies of our local group – the Milky Way and the great Andromeda spiral. The smaller members would be all but invisible, ghostly specks giving no indication of the billions of stars they contain.

Ten times further away, at a distance of 100 million light years from Earth, we can see that there is still a structure to the universe. There are many clusters of galaxies, similar to our own local group – some of these clusters are tens of millions of light years across.

The Andromeda spiral, the nearest major galaxy outside our own, is 2.2 million light years away.

RIGHT Part of the Virgo cluster 60 million light years away, possibly containing 1000 galaxies across 10 million light years of space.

But even here we have not reached the limit of order. The clusters are held together to form superclusters, hundreds of millions of light years in diameter.

On the largest imaginable scale, that of the whole universe, thousands of millions of light years across, there is a tracery that must surely form the grandest pattern ever conceived – strings of superclusters of galaxies stretching through space – echoes of the forces that created the universe itself.

LIGHTS IN THE DARKNESS

Through our travels across the universe we have seen objects that exist today and that we feel we can explain, with some degree of confidence at least.

But there are objects out in the depths of space that we can see today but that may no longer exist, such is the length of time their light has taken to travel to us.

These objects may have been some of the first to form out of the primeval chaos that followed the origin of the universe, objects that shine from the remote depths of time with an intensity that is extremely difficult, if not impossible, to explain.

What are these enigmatic powerhouses, some of them further from us than any other object? They are the quasars, sending shafts of light from the beginning of the cosmos, 15 thousand million years ago.

SECTION 1 SUMMARY

IN THE PRECEDING PAGES we have travelled to the limits of the observable universe. Its scale, both in time and distance, defies comprehension by the human mind. And yet a qualitative understanding of the nature of the universe is all that most of us need in order to appreciate and enjoy the majesty of the skies. The great nebulae, clusters and galaxies look as breathtaking to the layman as they do to the most eminent of astronomers and astrophysicists. Indeed, many of the most enjoyable studies of the heavens can be performed by amateur astronomers with no formal scientific training. Such pleasures as comet-hunting and meteor-watching can be indulged with relish by amateurs, and have the by-product that they can provide useful data for the professional community, and have done in the past.

But none of these observations can be interpreted correctly without a basic knowledge of the objects around us, the way in which they are related to each other and how they move. Observations, no matter how impressive, that cannot be described in terms of relationships to other heavenly bodies, are worse than useless. It is exactly this lack of understanding of the nature of the heavens that

held back the advancement of astronomy for thousands of years, and, to a certain extent, persisted even up to modern times.

So it is vital for anyone hoping to grasp the wonders of the firmament to have at least the basic facts about the universe at their disposal. I hope that by this stage of the book you will have become familiar with the building blocks of our universe and appreciate, to some extent at least, our place within it. But the information presented here is by no means the complete story. Many details, and some entire areas of the subject, have been omitted for the sake of clarity and in order to give you a broad basis on which to build, and one that is not over-complicated with technicalities.

All scientific subjects have to be described, at their lowest level, in terms of bewildering mathematics and mountains of numbers. Important as these are to the professional, they are of less significance for our purposes in the attempt to give a general background to astronomy. In fact, most of the figures provided in this book, interesting as they may be, are only really of use in describing the relative scale of the universe. The most important function of Section 1 is to give the reader a "feel" for the position of the Earth within the universe as a whole.

With no apology for restating what has gone before, here is a brief recapitulation of the basic structure of the universe, as astronomers believe it to be at present.

1. The Earth is a planet, just as Mercury, Venus, Mars and so on are planets. The notable difference between Earth and the other eight known planets is that it provides conditions that are suitable for life.

2. The nine planets all orbit our star, the Sun. Various other bodies also orbit the Sun, including the asteroids, or minor planets, which are mainly contained in a belt between the orbits of Mars and Jupiter. Outside the orbits of the planets we believe there is a vast sphere of icy objects, some of which fall towards the Sun to form comets. All of these objects, together with the Sun, form the family we refer to as the Solar System.

3. The Sun is a star, much the same as many others we see in the night sky. It is a very ordinary star, larger than some, smaller than others, appearing bright and important to us only because it is so close. It is likely that other stars have planets circling them, and some of these planets may support life.

4. All of the stars we see in the sky are part of one giant congregation that we call a galaxy. The name we give to our galaxy is the Milky Way, and it is in the shape of a flattened disk with a catherine-wheel structure, from which we derive the name for this type of galaxy;

Upper Sagittarius centred on the small Sagittarius Star Cloud.

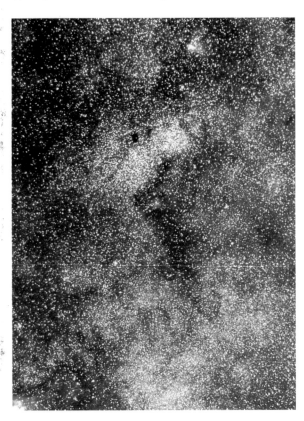

EARTH IN THE UNIVERSE

a spiral. Within the Milky Way there are many types of stars, some of which form loose associations, called open clusters, others of which are held closely together like massive balls of stars, called globular clusters, that form a great halo centred on the nucleus of the Milky Way. Also within our galaxy are clouds of gas and dust that we call nebulae, some of which shine because of light from nearby stars.

5. Far outside the Milky Way are countless other galaxies, stretching to the edge of the observable universe. Some of these are spirals, like our galaxy, but there are also various other shapes and sizes; the Milky Way happens to be rather larger than the average galaxy. A number of relatively close galaxies are held together gravitationally to form what we call the Local Group of galaxies.

6. When we look beyond the Local Group we can see that there are many such collections of galaxies. On an even larger scale these groups appear to form massive clusters or superclusters of galaxies. It has been suggested that these clusters may be linked in some way to form structures of unimaginable size: strings, or filaments, stretching across the universe itself.

Travelling from Earth to the edge of the universe in less than a page may not be good for the digestion, but it is worth trying to visualize the steps involved, even if you only get the general idea. An understanding of our place in the universe and the other objects that exist in it is invaluable for a greater appreciation of the cosmos.

An artist's impression of sunrise from Earth orbit.

SECTION 2

LOOKING AT THE NIGHT SKY

SO FAR WE'VE LOOKED at the many types of object that make up the universe – planets, stars, clusters, nebulae, galaxies and even more exotic objects. We've travelled from the Earth to the depths of space, as if we could just wander through the cosmos at will. But almost all our knowledge of the skies comes from looking at these objects from Earth, or from satellites in orbit.

Even our most adventurous projects – the Voyager spacecraft to the outer planets – are still in our backyard, by astronomical standards. And so we build ever more powerful telescopes to let us look further and further into space. In the next few pages we are going to see some of the most beautiful sights in the sky, photographed by the best equipment available to the modern astronomer.

But don't be disheartened if you want to look at the skies for yourself – many of the objects can be seen with small telescopes, binoculars or even the naked eye: much of the fun for the amateur astronomer is in finding your way around the sky and locating distant nebulae and galaxies. Imagine the excitement of looking at an object whose light left it before humans first appeared on the Earth!

Before we rush off across the light years there are a few things to explain, so that you get the most out of what is to come. If you only want to see the sights, then go straight to Starchart 1, but if you would like to understand why the skies change with the time of day and the seasons, why our starcharts are the shape they are, and why we use different equipment to observe different things – then read on.

THE CHANGING SKIES

Try to think in 3 dimensions; imagine the Earth floating in space and orbiting the Sun (*below*). The path that Earth takes around the Sun is in what is called the "plane of the Earth's orbit". Notice the line drawn through the north and south poles of the Earth – this is the Earth's axis – and that this line is tilted at an angle to the plane of the Earth's orbit (in fact it is tilted at an angle of 23.5 degrees to the plane, but that is not important for our purposes).

This tilt is the cause of summer and winter; when the Earth is in the position shown on the left of the illustration (*below*), then the northern hemisphere gets more sunshine (the Sun rises higher in the sky) and it is summer in the north; when the Earth is in the position shown on the right (six months later) it is summer in the south.

Now all of this may not seem very important to astronomers – most of them are looking at the sky when it is dark and the Sun is on the other side

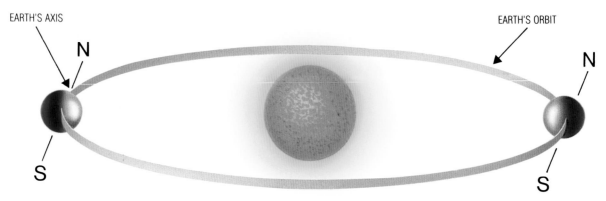

EARTH'S AXIS

N

S

SUMMER IN THE NORTH

EARTH'S ORBIT

N

S

SUMMER IN THE SOUTH

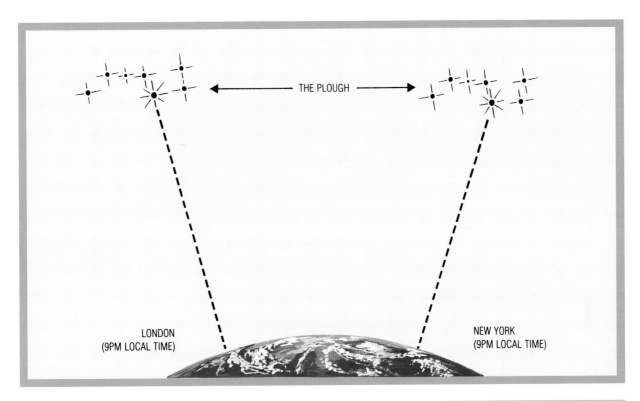

← THE PLOUGH →

LONDON
(9PM LOCAL TIME)

NEW YORK
(9PM LOCAL TIME)

Despite the fact that New York is 5 hours behind Greenwich Mean Time, London, the same stars will be visible to observers in both cities at the same local time.

of the Earth – but this is exactly why we see different stars in the summer to the ones we see in the winter; when the Earth is on the left we see the stars that are on that side of the Sun; similarly, when the Earth is on the right of the Sun we see the stars that are on that side of the Sun.

This may seem very straightforward, but it is important to realise that not only do the stars move across the sky during the night (because the Earth rotates on its axis once every day) but that different stars are seen during different seasons; so don't rush out into the countryside to see your favourite star cluster unless you're very sure that it's actually going to be there!

Another useful thing to remember is the effect that different time zones have on the position of objects in the sky. The reason for having various time zones is simply that people like to have daylight during the day and

darkness at night. This again may be obvious, but consider what it means; if the Sun is at its highest point in the sky at midday (local time) in London, then it will also be at its highest point at midday (local time) in New York.

Of course the same is true for any celestial object, and so, for example, if the Plough, in the constellation of Ursa Major, is at its highest point at 9pm (local time) in one time zone then it will also be at its highest point at 9pm (local time) for all other time zones.

To put it simply, whatever you can see from one place on Earth at a time of night, you can see from anywhere else at the same local time, assuming you are in the same hemisphere, as shown in the diagram *(above)*.

Of course, the skies change in appearance not only because of the Earth's motion, but because of our own position on the Earth's surface; for people very far north, only those stars in the northern part of the sky are visible during the year; for those in the far south, only southern stars can be seen; observers on the equator will be able to see all of the sky at various times of the year.

Astronomical Unit

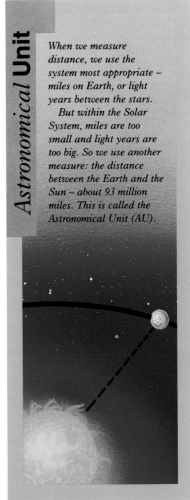

When we measure distance, we use the system most appropriate – miles on Earth, or light years between the stars.

But within the Solar System, miles are too small and light years are too big. So we use another measure: the distance between the Earth and the Sun – about 93 million miles. This is called the Astronomical Unit (AU).

NAMING CONVENTIONS

THERE ARE VARIOUS CATALOGUES of "deep sky objects" which are used by astronomers. These are lists of nebulae, open and globular star clusters and galaxies. The two most commonly used are the Messier Catalogue and the New General Catalogue. Messier was a French astronomer whose speciality was hunting for comets, which often appear as faint hazy dots, and so he compiled his catalogue of "Messier objects" in order to avoid confusing nebulae, clusters and galaxies (which can also appear as faint hazy dots) with genuine comets. Charles Messier published his catalogue between 1771 and 1784.

The New General Catalogue (NGC) was prepared by J. L. E. Dryer and published in 1888. This contains many more objects than Messier's but some objects appear in both. In practice we tend to use Messier's catalogue numbers if they exist and NGC numbers for other objects.

The starcharts in this book use the same convention, so, for example, the Crab Nebula on Starchart 3 is listed as M1 – the first object in Messier's catalogue – but the Helix Nebula on Starchart 2 was not listed by Messier and is described as NGC 7293. These M and NGC numbers are particularly useful for clusters and galaxies because many of them are not given individual names.

DISTANCES AND SIZES OF OBJECTS

Because of the vast distances between objects in the universe it is very difficult to accurately measure distances and sizes. Even the closest stars appear only as points of light.

One method of measuring the distance to nearby stars is called "trigonometric parallax", which uses the fact that close stars appear to move very slightly over the course of the year because of the Earth's motion around the Sun *(right)*.

Unfortunately this is only useful to a distance of a few hundred light years because the apparent movement of even the closest stars is so small. There are many other methods for measuring distances to faraway objects but as the distance increases the uncertainty in the accuracy of the measurement also increases.

For this reason it is important to use the figures given in this book for

Greek Alphabet

Most of the brightest stars have been given proper names, such as Sirius which is the brightest star in the sky.

But the majority of stars have no individual names and so we use letters of the Greek alphabet to identify them. However, there are far too many stars to use only these letters, so one Greek letter is assigned to each of the brightest stars in each constellation. On this basis, Sirius is also known as alpha (α) Canis Majoris, and the second brightest star in Canis Major is beta (β) Canis Majoris, and so on.

Similarly, Antones, the brightest star in the constellation of Scorpio, is also known as alpha Scorpii.

As there are 24 letters in the Greek alphabet, and 88 constellations in the sky, we can therefore identify 2112 stars by this method – quite enough for most people.

THE GREEK ALPHABET		
Capitals		Small
A	alpha	α
B	beta	β
Γ	gamma	γ
Δ	delta	δ
E	epsilon	ε
Z	zeta	ζ
H	eta	η
Θ	theta	θ
I	iota	ι
K	kappa	κ
Λ	lambda	λ
M	mu	μ
N	nu	ν
Ξ	xi	ξ
O	omicron	ο
Π	pi	π
Ρ	rho	ρ
Σ	sigma	σ
T	tau	τ
Y	upsilon	υ
Φ	phi	φ
X	chi	χ
Ψ	psi	ψ
Ω	omega	ω

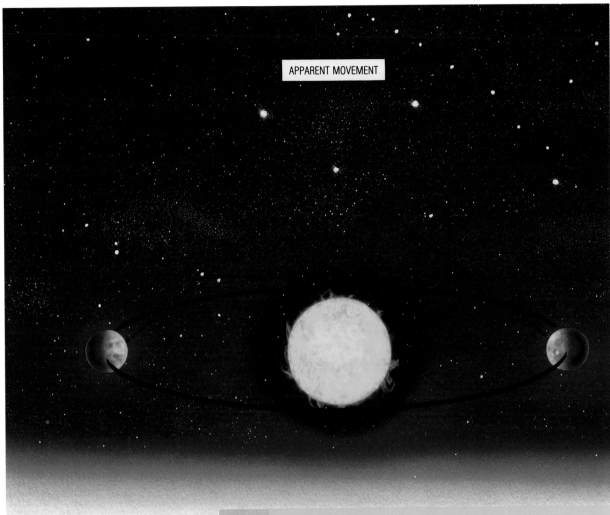

APPARENT MOVEMENT

distance and size, as a guide and not as exact measurements. The value of these figures is in giving some idea of the scale of the universe and the relationship between objects in it; there are about ten stars within ten light years of the Sun; the Milky Way is about 100 thousand light years from one end to the other and we are about 20 thousand light years in from the edge, so nothing inside the galaxy is going to be more than about 80 thousand light years away; the nearest major galaxy is just over 2 million light years from us; the nearest quasars are (probably) some 3000 million light years away and the most distant may be as far away as 15 thousand million light years.

Remember that there is still much discussion between astronomers about the accuracy of these enormous figures and they are constantly being reviewed.

The Parsec

Earlier in the book we saw that the closer stars appear to move against the background of stars, as the Earth moves in its orbit around the Sun. This apparent movement is called "trigonometric parallax".

The concept of the Parsec uses this – it is defined as "the distance of a star which has a trigonometrical parallax of one second of arc." The name Parsec is derived from the key words of the definition: Parallax and Second. The actual distance of a star that is one parsec from Earth is 3.26 light years, so 1 Parsec = 3.26 light years.

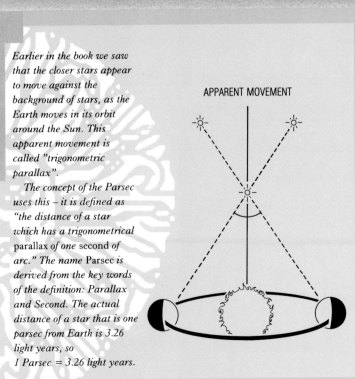

APPARENT MOVEMENT

SYSTEMS OF MEASUREMENT

MOST PEOPLE ARE FAMILIAR with the way positions on Earth can be fixed using latitude and longitude. This picture of the Earth (*right*), taken by the Insat 1B Satellite, has a grid drawn on it to show example lines of latitude (running north-south) and of longitude (running east-west).

Latitude is measured in degrees from the equator, which is 0 degrees, to the poles, which are 90 degrees north or south. Longitude is also measured in degrees, east or west of the "Greenwich Meridian" (an imaginary line on the Earth's surface, drawn through the north and south poles and Greenwich, London, England), which is at 0 degrees.

You will see that the starcharts that follow are marked with a grid, similar to the one drawn on the picture of Earth, which gives the astronomical

The Earth seen from space by the Insat 1B satellite, with example lines of latitude and longitude superimposed.

Angular Size

The diameter of astronomical objects, or the distance between them in the sky, is usually measured in degrees of arc. The Sun and Moon, for example, are both half a degree in diameter. Relative positions of the stars are often described in terms of the number of degrees between them. As a rough guide to angular sizes, hold your clenched fist at arm's length, palm down – the distance across your knuckles is about six to seven degrees.

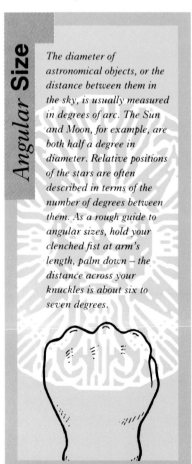

equivalents of latitude and longitude – if you take a serious interest in astronomical observation, you will need to become familiar with these coordinates, since they are always used when describing the position of an object in the sky.

The astronomical equivalent of latitude on Earth is declination (Dec), which is given in degrees and minutes of angles. This is a measure of an object's position in the sky, north or south of the celestial equator. The value for declination is the first figure given beneath each of the photographs alongside the starcharts: use this to find where the object photographed is on the north-south axis.

The astronomical equivalent of longitude is the right ascension (RA),

and is measured in hours, minutes and seconds of time, rather than degrees of angles. These units are convenient to use because the day is divided into 24 hours, and the stars appear to move across the sky once a day. So if we define a standard point in the sky (the first point of Aries), we measure the time difference between our standard point and any other object appearing on the same meridian – this period of time being the right ascension of the object concerned.

Use the figure for the right ascension to fix an object's position on the east-west coordinate. The whole procedure is exactly the same as plotting the position of a city on a map of the Earth using its latitude and longitude.

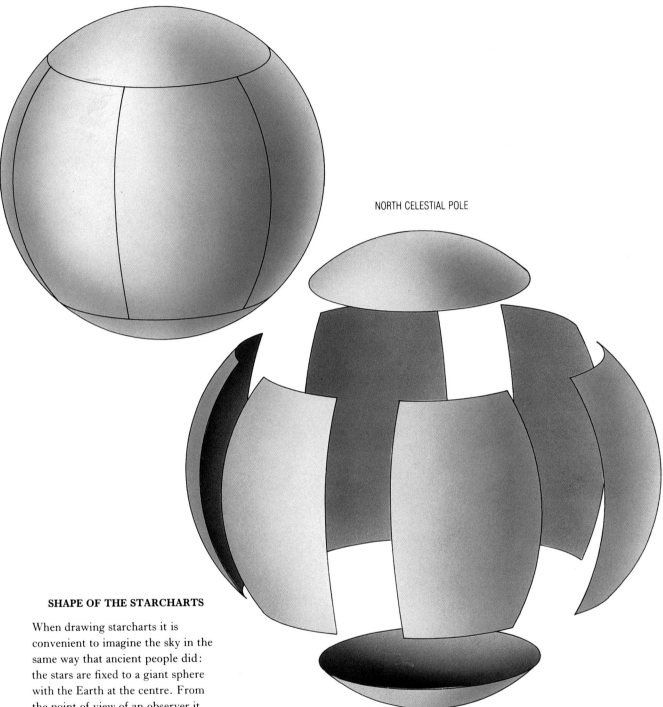

NORTH CELESTIAL POLE

SOUTH CELESTIAL POLE

SHAPE OF THE STARCHARTS

When drawing starcharts it is convenient to imagine the sky in the same way that ancient people did: the stars are fixed to a giant sphere with the Earth at the centre. From the point of view of an observer it really doesn't matter how far away an object is, only where in the sky it can be found. Imagine then that we are on the inside of this sphere.

Obviously it is impossible to draw the whole of the sphere on a single page, so we have divided the sky into eight sections; think of the way you might peel an orange, by cutting off the top and bottom and then slicing the remaining peel at equal intervals around it (*see above*).

If the top of the orange is north, and the bottom is south, then we have two circular charts representing the stars around the north and south poles. The other six charts each have a line across the centre, representing five hours of right ascension around the celestial equator and cover an area of the sky from 60 degrees North to 60 degrees South.

The starcharts each represent an area of the sky five hours of right ascension in width, so overlap each adjoining chart by one hour of right ascension.

DEGREES OF DIFFICULTY

THERE ARE MANY OCCASIONS when the word "degree" is used in astronomy, and although we are familiar with the word in everyday use its meaning may be somewhat confusing in this context. There are two distinct areas where it appears in this book; "degrees of arc" and "degrees of temperature".

An object in the sky can be described in terms of its position relative to another object, and this position is expressed in "degrees of arc".

The temperature of a planet, star, nebula and other heavenly body, may be measured in degrees Kelvin, Celsius (or centigrade) or –it is unlikely, but just possible – in Fahrenheit.

These conventions are described in more detail below in a effort to avoid any confusion that may arise from the use of the term "degrees" in the description of objects.

DEGREES OF ARC

Most people know that a circle is divided up into 360 "degrees of arc". This allows us to specify the position of any one of 360 points around the circumference of the circle. One common application of this is the method of determining a position on the Earth's surface, using latitude (north of south of the equator) and longitude (east or west of the Greenwich meridian). But using degrees alone does not give us the accuracy we require to pinpoint a position exactly, and so degrees of arc are sub-divided into minutes of arc (60 minutes in every degree), and minutes of arc are sub-divided into seconds of arc (60 seconds in every minute). If we need even more precision we use decimals of a second of arc.

This circular, or angular, measure is widely used in astronomy, where, as you can see from the shape of the starcharts, it is more convenient to draw curves or arcs of circles than it is to draw straight lines. Hence, you might find a piece of astronomical text describing "the distance between the two pointer stars in the Great Bear, Dubhe and Merak, is about 5 degrees". This means that a line

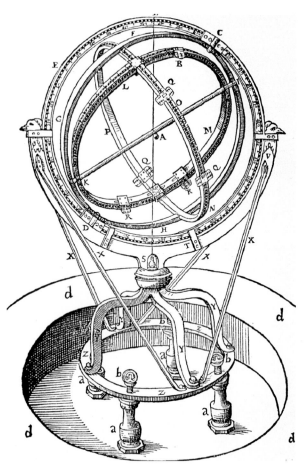

Early astronomers used instruments such as this armillary to measure the position of objects in the sky.

drawn on a starchart between the stars Dubhe and Merak would form an arc that is about five degrees in length, or their angular separation is about five degrees of arc.

This is quite straightforward, but might be slightly confusing if you are not familiar with the convention. As you will see, there is no mysterious reason for measuring positions in this way – it is simply the easiest way of pin pointing where something is in the sky.

The astronomical equivalent of latitude on Earth is declination (Dec). This is a measure of an object's position in the sky, north or south of the celestial equator. The value for declination is the first figure given beneath each of the photographs alongside the starcharts that follow: use this to find where the object photographed is on the north-south axis. Then take the second figure – the right ascension (RA) – to fix its position on the east-west coordinate. The procedure is exactly the same as plotting the position of a city on a map of the Earth using its latitude and longitude. Both degrees of declination and hours of right ascension are sub-divided into minutes and

---

Interpreter

M82	(NGC 3034)	RA 09h 55.8m	Dec +69° 41′
Messier Catalogue Number	New General Catalogue Number	Right Ascension in hours and minutes	Declination in degrees and minutes; + = north of celestial equator; − = south

Use this key to interpret the figues given beneath the photographs in the starchart section that follows. The values for right ascension (RA) and declination (Dec) can be used to track an object down in the sky.

ABSOLUTE

zero K   +273.16 K   +373.16 K

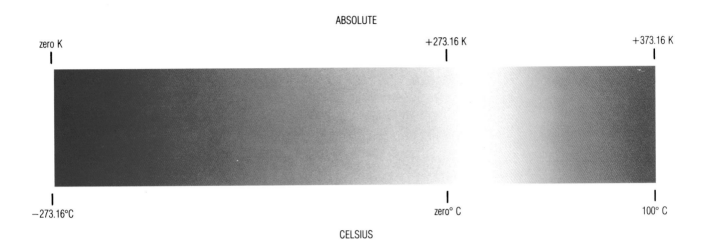

−273.16°C   zero° C   100° C

CELSIUS

seconds, but these are measures of angles, in the case of declination, and time, when applied to right ascension.

Degrees, minutes and seconds of arc (not given on the photographs) are useful when the position of one object in the sky relative to another, rather than its position in the sky. Such measurements are valuable when describing planetary positions and their movements relative to the background stars: an astronomer might say, for example, that a particular planet can be found a certain number of degrees, minutes and seconds north, south, east or west of a special star.

DEGREES OF TEMPERATURE

The difference between the use of the word "degree" for measuring the length of an arc of a circle, and its use in measuring temperature is fairly obvious. But there are various "scales" of temperature and a measurement of degrees on one scale may not represent the same temperature as the same measurement on another scale. Here is a brief guide to the reasons for using different temperature scales, and the implications they have in astronomy.

The Celsius, or Centigrade, scale of temperature is based on the melting point of ice and the boiling point of water, and was proposed by a Swedish scientist, Celsius, in the 18th century. This scale defines the lower fixed point – the melting point of ice at one atmospheric pressure (normal pressure at sea level) – to be zero degrees Celsius (abbreviated C), and the upper fixed point – the temperature of steam over boiling water at one atmospheric pressure – to be 100 degrees C. This scale is particularly useful for everyday measurements, the majority of which fall within this range.

The Absolute, or Thermodynamic, scale of temperature is based on the second law of thermodynamics, and temperatures on this scale are measured in degrees K, after Lord Kelvin who first

proposed its use. The lower fixed point of the Absolute scale, zero K, is called absolute zero and is the temperature at which all thermal motion vanishes in matter, or more simply, the point at which no more heat can be extracted – the coldest temperature possible. Absolute zero is equivalent to −273.16 on the Celsius scale, so zero K = −273.16 degrees C. Because the actual interval between one degree and the next is the same on both scales this means a change of temperature of, for example, 10 degrees on the Celsius scale is also a change of 10 degrees on the Absolute scale, although the actual value measured for any temperature will vary between the two by 273.16 degrees. This also means the zero degrees Celsius is equivalent to 273.16 K.

The Fahrenheit scale of temperature was proposed by a German physicist, Fahrenheit, in the early 18th century. It defines the lower fixed point, that of melting ice, to be 32 degrees F, and the upper fixed point, boiling water, to be 212 degrees F. This scale is not generally used for measuring temperatures in astronomy.

Both the Celsius and Absolute scales are commonly used to describe the temperature of astronomical bodies, and it is sometimes important to identify which is being applied. As we have seen, the numerical difference between the value of temperatures measured on the two scales is 273.16 degrees, but the actual interval between one degree and the next is the same on both.

It is necessary to specify which of the scales is being used when the temperature being measured is in the order of tens or hundreds of degrees. For example, if the surface temperature of Mars is measured on the Celsius scale then it is about −23 degrees C, but on the Absolute scale this equates to 250.16 K – a substantial difference if you don't know which scale you are using. However, when discussing the temperature of the core of a star which is tens of millions of degrees, then a difference of 273.16 degrees is really too small to measure, and it doesn't matter which scale is being used.

WHAT YOU NEED TO LOOK AT THE NIGHT SKY

FOR THE NEWCOMER TO astronomy, the choice of optical equipment can be bewildering. But don't despair – there are very simple rules for choosing your equipment.

First, there is no point in buying an expensive telescope until you know that you are going to enjoy astronomy, and you know the sky well enough to be able to use a telescope effectively.

Second, there are so many different areas of astronomy – comet hunting, meteor watching, observing variable stars, deep-sky objects, and many more – that you won't know what type of telescope you need until you have picked a subject. Undoubtedly the most useful first piece of optical equipment for the beginner is a pair of binoculars.

But again, there is a wide choice of binoculars, and it is important to choose the most effective type. A common mistake is to assume that the higher the magnification the better. The problem is that as the magnification increases the amount of light collected by the instrument decreases, so the object becomes fainter. The best choice is a general-purpose pair, such as 7 × 50 (this means a magnification of 7, and an object glass – the front lens – 50mm in diameter).

It is possible to buy "astronomical binoculars", such as 20 × 70, but these are expensive, heavy and must be mounted on a tripod – not worth the trouble to start with. A basic pair of 7 × 50 are perfectly good enough to see beautiful star fields, loose

Binoculars are undoubtedly the most effective piece of equipment for the amateur astronomer who is just beginning to discover the skies – portable, with a wide field of view, and easy to use.

clusters and bright nebulae. They are also very portable.

Once you decide to buy a telescope there are numerous varieties, and all have their advantages and disadvantages. The basic types are described below.

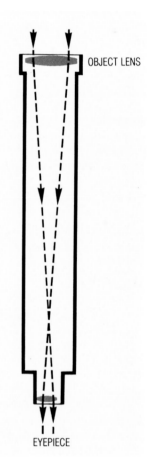

OBJECT LENS

EYEPIECE

The refracting telescope is capable of high magnification for its size, but has relatively low light-collecting power, so is best used for looking at bright objects, such as planets and large clusters.

The Refractor. Essentially, this consists of two lenses; a large object glass (or object lens) at the front, and a small lens or eyepiece at the rear. The eyepiece can usually be changed to provide different magnifications.

The advantages of this type of telescope are the excellent images that can be seen – planets and double

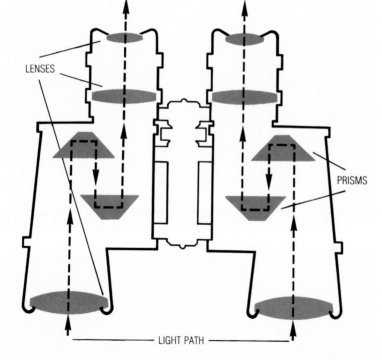

LENSES

PRISMS

LIGHT PATH

stars, for example – and the fact that there is not much to go wrong with them. Disadvantages are that refractors tend to be large and cumbersome, and the typical tripod stands are difficult to set up properly and therefore not easily portable.

The Reflector. This is the other main type of telescope, although there are many variations on the reflector. The two most common ones are the "Cassegrain" and the "Newtonian". All reflectors work on the same principle: they have a "main" or "primary" mirror at the rear end of the telescope tube that collects the light from an object. This light is then focused onto a "secondary" mirror from where it is reflected into the eyepiece.

The main difference between Cassegrains and Newtonians is that the Cassegrain reflects light from the

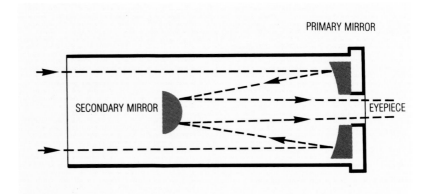

The Cassegrain reflector is one of the most popular telescopes because of its combination of light-collecting power and portability – a good all-round instrument.

secondary mirror to the eyepiece through a hole in the centre of the primary mirror, and the Newtonian reflects light from the secondary through the side of the telescope. The Cassegrain tends to be the most compact type of telescope and is therefore easily portable, but does not produce such clear images as other telescopes. Newtonians are

probably the cheapest for their size and collect more light than other telescopes of the same cost. This means that they are good for viewing faint deep-sky objects, such as nebulae and galaxies. Unfortunately though, they are quite delicate and the alignment of the mirrors can easily be upset.

Before choosing your telescope, remember to think about your own priorities – portability, photography perhaps, and, of course, cost.

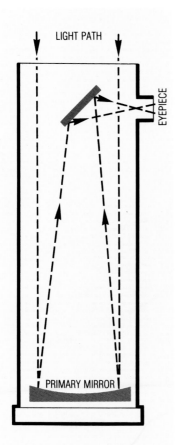

The Newtonian reflecting telescope has the best light-collecting power of all telescopes, so is good for looking at faint objects such as nebulae and galaxies.

Telescopic Image Inversion

When you first look through an astronomical telescope you will notice that everything looks different from the view in binoculars or in telescopes used to look at things on Earth. The difference is that everything's upside down.
This is because the lenses in these telescopes cause the image to be inverted. This can easily be corrected by
adding an extra lens to the telescope, but lenses reflect some light out of the instrument and this is the last thing that astronomers want – we need all the light we can get.
It takes a little time to get used to this effect, so experiment with familiar objects on Earth before you turn your attention to the skies.

VISUAL IMAGE

TELESCOPIC IMAGE

HINTS FOR PRACTICAL ASTRONOMY

LOOKING AT THE SKY is simply a matter of pointing your eyes, binoculars or telescope in the right direction – that's obvious. But without a little preparation you may see nothing at all, or not understand what you are looking at. This seems simple enough – but there are all sorts of simple things that are easy to overlook if you are not familiar with the subject.

So far in this book we have described the major objects that occur in the universe, and the Earth's place in it. In the rest of this section we will show photographs of some of the more visually impressive of these objects and provide starcharts to show the stars and how they are divided into constellations. As has been said, these photographs were taken with some of the most sophisticated equipment available to modern astronomers, and the amateur astronomer is unlikely to have access to such splendid and advanced instruments.

Nevertheless a vast amount can be seen, with even the most modest of binoculars and telescopes. In fact there is so much to be seen that many books are published specifically for the amateur observer and one of these will be invaluable if you hope to find most of the wonders of the skies. They are widely available and range from those intended for the casual observer using binoculars, to those for the serious amateur astronomer which contain detailed star maps with exact coordinates of the major deep sky objects.

Once you have your binoculars or telescope, it is worth spending a little time looking at simple objects, such as the Moon, to familiarise yourself with the operation of the equipment.

This is particulary true for telescopes that are mounted on stands – these are intended to make observation easier, but may give confusing results to begin with. Also, telescopes invert the image you see,

so some practice in daylight will help to prepare you for what you will see at night. Remember, when you are outside on a dark night the last thing you want to do is to use a light to find out how your telescope works – this will ruin your night vision until your eyes become accustomed to the dark again. If you need to take a light with you, cover it with a red filter (red paper or plastic will do) as this has little effect on night vision.

Most small telescopes have a "finderscope" – that is a small telescope, attached to the main one, that gives a wide field of vision and allows you to find the general area of the sky that contains the object you are looking for. This finderscope will probably have a cross-hair, just like a telescopic sight, that lets you pinpoint the exact spot you want: However, when you first get your

telescope this finderscope needs to be adjusted so that it is perfectly aligned with the main scope. It is worth taking care to do this properly, as it will save you a great deal of time when observing. Check it regularly to make sure it is still aligned.

The lenses of your telescope are the most important part of the equipment and it is vital to make sure that they are covered by the lens caps provided whenever the telescope is not in use. If anything does get on the lenses, then avoid the urge to clean it off – just about everything you could do to clean the lenses is likely to cause more harm, and the odd fingerprint will have little effect on your view, whereas a scratched lens could ruin the instrument. Having told you to keep lens caps on whenever possible, don't forget to take them off before you start observing – not an uncommon mistake, and it really does make you feel very silly.

When you actually get outside, a number of things can spoil your evening's viewing. Try to get away from as much light as possible – if you are in your back garden turn off all the lights at the back of the house. Once you are outside you will notice that your night vision will improve in a matter of minutes, but any sudden bright light will spoil the effect immediately.

One common cause of bad visibility is moisture on the lenses. This can easily happen if "room-temperature" telescopes or binoculars are taken out into cold night air and water condenses on them. This can easily be avoided by leaving the instrument in a cold place for a little while before you start viewing.

The longer you spend studying the sky during an evening, the better your night vision will become and the more you will see. But observing is, by its very nature, often cold; it can be uncomfortable, unless you prepare yourself properly. So dress warmly and use a comfortable seat that gives good position for looking into the eyepiece.

Now you are ready to explore the universe – or are you? By the time you've set up your equipment, made yourself comfortable and your eyes are accustomed to the dark, you've probably forgotten what it was you were going to look at, and almost certainly where it is in the sky. You can't go back inside to check because you will ruin your night vision. The answer is to take your starcharts, or observer's guide, with you and have a red light to read by.

This may seem an awful lot of fuss and bother, but it only takes a few minutes and makes the difference between a stiff neck, a bad temper, and a miserable night, or seeing the stunning beauty of the heavens. After all, since it's taken fifteen thousand million years to prepare this light-show, is a few minutes preparation really that long?

STARCHART 1

How to use the starcharts
Think of the starcharts as route maps of the night sky; they do not show every object – to do so would be almost impossible. If you want to find one of the deep sky objects shown in the accompanying photographs, use the coordinates given below each one – an interpreter is given on page 70.

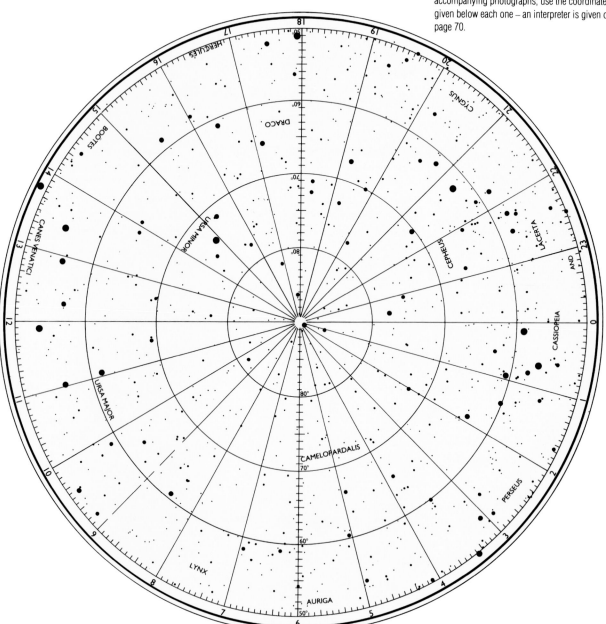

1.
"THE PLOUGH" IN URSA MAJOR

We start our exploration of the skies with one of the most well-known constellations. Astronomers use the ancient name, Ursa Major, to describe this group of stars, but it is more widely known by the English translation of the Latin, the Great Bear. Even more common are the nicknames the Plough and the Big Dipper, although these are generally used to describe the seven brightest stars, shown in the photograph, which only make up part of the whole constellation.

Because these seven stars are so easy to find in the sky, they form a useful starting point from which to find other stars: in particular, the Pole Star, Polaris. The two bright stars of the Plough, on the right of the photograph, appear on the starchart at right ascension 11. Follow this line along towards the centre and you will find the star Polaris almost in the middle. This is sometimes called the North Star because it is very close to the North Celestial Pole.

A useful thing to note is that for any one place in the northern hemisphere Polaris is always in the same position in the sky, and so after you find it once you will always have a fixed point from which to find other stars. Also, you will always know which direction is north. The only change in the position of Polaris is in its height (elevation) above the horizon when you move north or south; the further north you go, the higher Polaris is in the sky. However, this isn't much use to people in most of the southern hemisphere because Polaris is always below the horizon.

1. The Plough or Big Dipper, pointer to Polaris, the North Star.

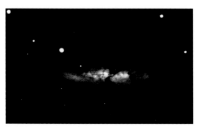

2. M82 (NGC 3034) RA 09h 55.8m Dec. +69° 41′

2.
GALAXIES M81 AND M82 IN URSA MAJOR

This pair of galaxies is not far from the two stars in the Plough, which we use to find Polaris. M81 is a spiral galaxy and M82 is an irregular galaxy. The two appear to be linked and are 8.5 million light years from Earth. They are part of a small cluster of galaxies that is centred about 7 million light years away – that's no more than a stone's throw in astronomical terms!

The photograph of M81 has been processed through a range of filters to highlight the natural colours in order to show the distribution of different types of stars; the old red stars at the centre, the young blue stars along the spiral arms.

M82 is one of those objects that has baffled astronomers for years; various theories have suggested that it is expanding while some say it is contracting – nobody is really sure what it is doing. This is not unusual in astronomy.

2. M81 (NGC 3031) RA 09h 55.6m Dec. +69° 04′

STARCHART 2

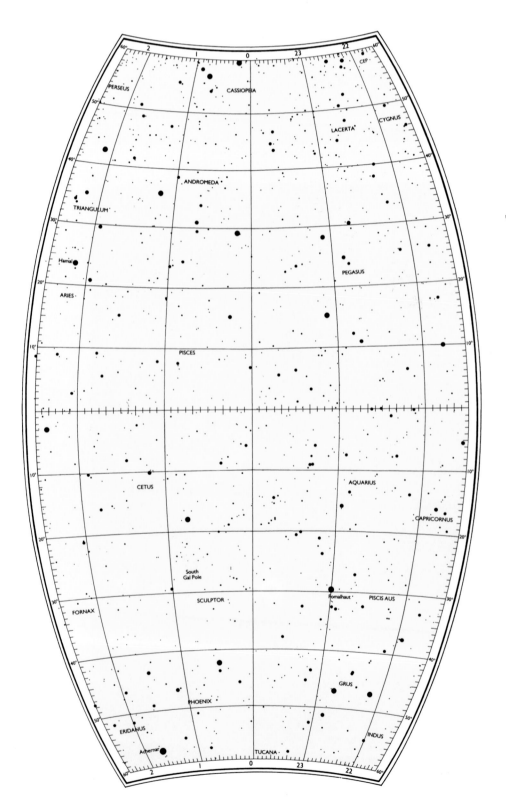

1.
THE "GREAT NEBULA" IN ANDROMEDA, M31

This is not in fact a nebula, but a galaxy. At the time when Messier was compiling his catalogue he did not know there were galaxies outside our own galaxy, the Milky Way – everything was thought to be part of one great cloud of stars – and so he listed all of these misty patches as nebulae.

M31 is one of the most famous of them and somehow the word nebula has stuck. This is the closest major galaxy to our own, at a distance of some 2.2 million light years, it's approximately 150,000 light years across and is a member of our local group of galaxies. Our own galaxy would probably look very much like this, if we could take a picture of it from outside.

2. M33 (NGC 598) RA 01h 33.9m Dec. +30° 39'

2.
A SPIRAL GALAXY IN TRIANGULUM, M33

Another member of our local group of galaxies, some 2.4 million light years away. The diameter of M33 is about 40,000 light years and it has a

1. M31 (NGC 224) RA 00h 42.7m Dec. +41° 16'

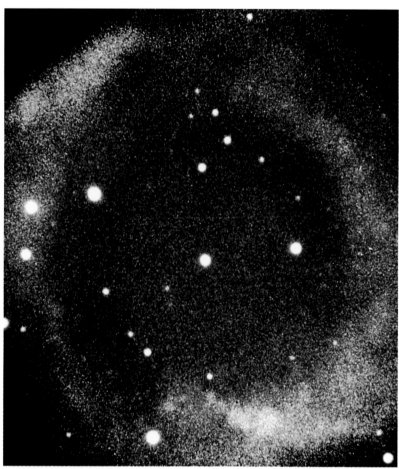

3. NGC 7293 RA 22h 29.6m Dec. −20° 48′

mass some 15,000 million times that of our Sun.

The picture was taken through various coloured filters and shows the older red and yellow stars at the centre, the young blue stars in the spiral arms, and several giant clouds of hydrogen gas (which look pink) where star formation is taking place.

3.
THE "HELIX" NEBULA IN AQUARIUS, NGC 7293

This object is of the type known as "planetary nebulae". These are nothing to do with planets, but are so-called because that is what they looked like to 19th-century astronomers. In reality, this nebula is a cloud of gas that is expanding away from the central star and shines by light from that star.

The shell of gas is ejected from the central star in the later stages of its life when it becomes unstable. It is thought that most low-mass stars like this one, including our own Sun, will produce this expanding shell of gas in the dying years of their lives. In this case, the helix shape, which gives rise to the nebula's name, might be due to a second star orbiting the central one – but this is too small to be seen.

4.
A SPIRAL GALAXY IN SCULPTOR, NGC 253

This true colour photograph shows a spiral galaxy almost edge-on. Again the redness of the central region, or nucleus indicates older stars, and the blue of the spiral arms comes from young hot stars. The galaxy is about 10 million light years away and is part of a small cluster of galaxies, which is generally known as the Sculptor Group.

4. NGC 253 RA 00h 47.6m Dec. −25° 17′

STARCHART 3

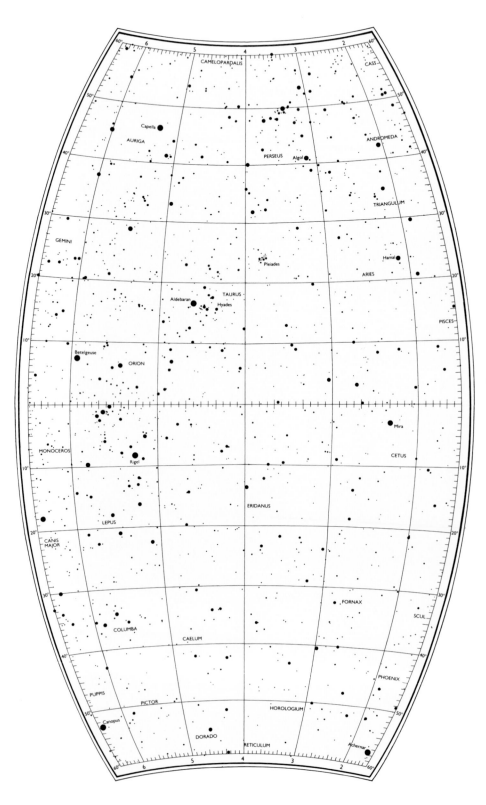

1. The Horsehead Nebula RA 05h 40.9m
Dec. −02° 28'

1.

THE HORSEHEAD NEBULA IN ORION

The bright star at the top of the photograph is Zeta Orionis, the left-most star in the Belt of Orion. Around it can be seen various areas of nebulosity – clouds of hot gas. Slightly below the centre is a small dark area that is caused by a cold dust cloud in front of the hot gas. This dark area has the shape of a horse's head, from which the nebula gets its name.

2.

THE GREAT NEBULA IN ORION, M42

Just below the three stars that make up the "Belt of Orion" are a number of fainter stars that constitute the "Sword of Orion". Around these stars you can see, even with the naked eye,

2. M42 RA 05h 35.4m Dec. −05° 27′

a fine gaseous nebula. This is a cloud of hot gas and dust inside which new stars are forming.

We see this nebula both by reflected starlight from dust in the cloud, and also by emission of energy from gas that has been heated by the proto-stars within the nebula. M42 is some 1600 light years from Earth.

3. M45 RA 03h 47.0m Dec. +24° 07'

3.
THE PLEIADES IN TAURUS, M45

Although generally described as an "open cluster", the Pleiades are in fact a more evolved example of a gaseous nebula, of the type described above in Orion. On closer inspection you can see the young, hot blue stars surrounded by the remains of the nebula from which they are in the process of condensing.

The gravitational attraction of stars within this type of cluster is not sufficient to hold them in formation for more than about 100 million years, so we know the maximum age of these stars cannot be greater than this. In fact the Pleiades are about 60 million years old. With the naked eye it is only possible to see a maximum of seven stars in the cluster, but in fact there are more than two hundred stars in the group.

4.
THE CRAB NEBULA IN TAURUS, M1

Unlike M42 and M45, which are new stars in the process of formation, the Crab Nebula is at the other end of the stellar evolutionary scale. This

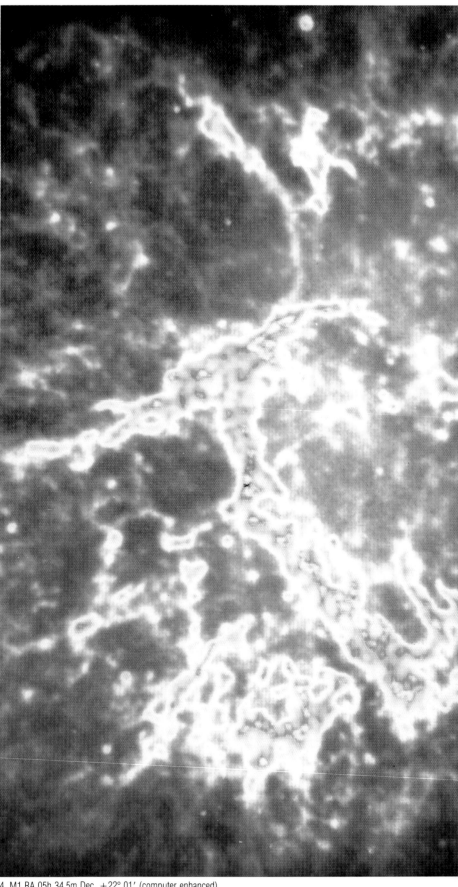

4. M1 RA 05h 34.5m Dec. +22° 01' (computer enhanced).

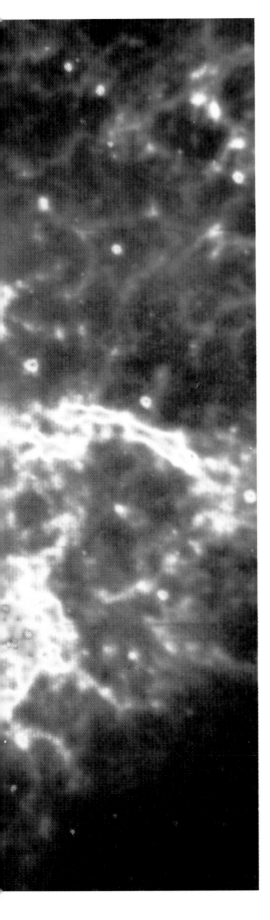

5. *H* and *Chi* Persei cluster
RA 02h 17.2m Dec. +56° 55′

6. The Hyades RA 04h 25.0m
Dec. +17° 00′

cosmic lighthouse, flashing out intermittent bursts of energy – thus the name "pulsar".

5.
THE DOUBLE CLUSTER IN PERSEUS, *H* AND *CHI* PERSEI

These two open clusters are just visible with the naked eye, as a misty patch. Each contains over 300 young stars, *h* being some 10 million years old, and *chi* about 15 million years old. They are roughly 6500 light years away from Earth.

6.
THE HYADES IN TAURUS

is the result of one of the most spectacular events in the universe. Called a supernova, this is when a massive star explodes, at which time the star outshines the entire combined radiation of the galaxy in which it occurs.

The Crab is thought to be the remains of the supernova observed by the Chinese in the year 1054. All that remains of the original star is a spinning neutron star, known as a pulsar. This is an object of unimaginable density – a teaspoonful of its material would weigh almost 1000 million tonnes – that emits an intense beam of radiation. Because it is spinning, it looks rather like a

Although less spectacular than some other open clusters, the Hyades are one of the most important to astronomers – at a distance of only 147 light years it is the nearest open cluster to Earth. The significance of this is that the motion of these stars through space can actually be observed and measured.

A technique, called the Moving Cluster Method, can then be used to calculate the distance of the cluster. By comparing the brightness of these stars with that of similar ones in very remote clusters, the distance to those faraway objects can be found. This is a very useful method for discovering the size of our galaxy.

STARCHART 4

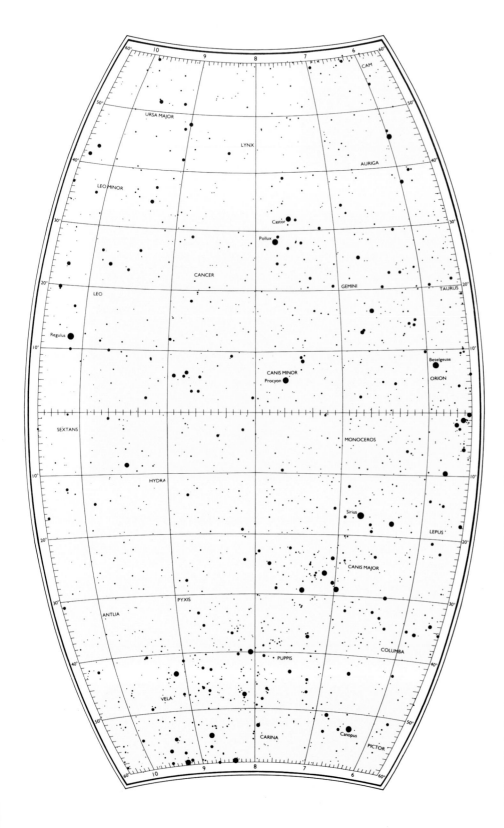

1. M44 RA 08h 40.1m Dec. +19° 40′

1.
THE "BEEHIVE" STAR CLUSTER IN CANCER, M44

This is an open cluster of stars, known both as the "Beehive" and "Praesepe". Containing many doubles and triangles of stars, this cluster is easy to see with good binoculars or a small telescope, and can just about be seen with the naked eye as a fuzzy spot since it is more than one degree in diameter.

In fact, this cluster, with some 300

stars, is one of the nearest of its type to Earth, at around 500 light years distance from us. It is believed to be about 650 million years old.

2.
AN OPEN CLUSTER IN CANIS MAJOR, M41

This cluster, in the constellation of Canis Major, is similar to M44, above, but is smaller, with some 100 stars. Particularly attractive and colourful, it is about 1600 light years from Earth.

2. M41 RA 06h 46.0m Dec. −20° 44′

3.
AN OPEN CLUSTER IN PUPIS, M46, AND PLANETARY NEBULA

This photograph shows not only an open cluster of stars but, just above the centre, a planetary nebula as well. The nebula is not associated with the cluster and is, in fact, about three times further away. It is another example of an expanding shell of gas which has been ejected from a dying, central star. This shows well why the name "planetary" was given to this type of nebula.

4.
THE "ROSETTE" NEBULA IN MONOCEROS, NGC 2244

This nebula is a cloud of hot gas, surrounding a central cluster of stars. The cluster causes the heating of the gas and because of the distinctive red

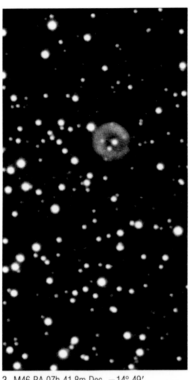

3. M46 RA 07h 41.8m Dec. −14° 49′

colour we can tell that it is hydrogen. The stars are thought to be very young – perhaps less than half a million years old. The cluster and nebula are about 4500 light years from Earth.

5.
THE "DOG STAR" SIRIUS IN CANIS MAJOR

Sirius (*bottom right*) is the brightest star in the sky and shows in this photograph against a dense background of stars. The constellation of Canis Major is one of the most prominent in southern skies.

Sirius is what is known as a binary star; it is part of a two-star system, in which both stars orbit around their common centre of gravity. The companion star is a "white dwarf" and is too small to see without a very large telescope.

4. NGC 2244 RA 06h 33.4m Dec. +04° 03′

5. Sirius RA 06h 45.1m Dec. −16° 43′

STARCHART 5

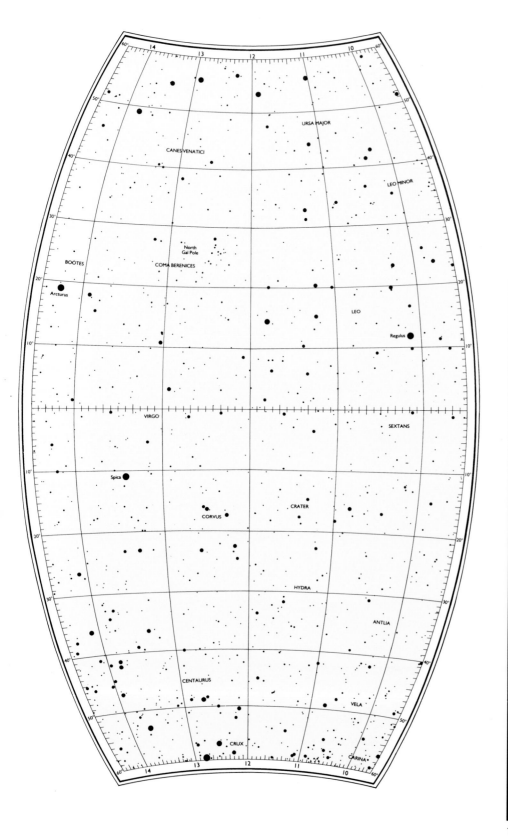

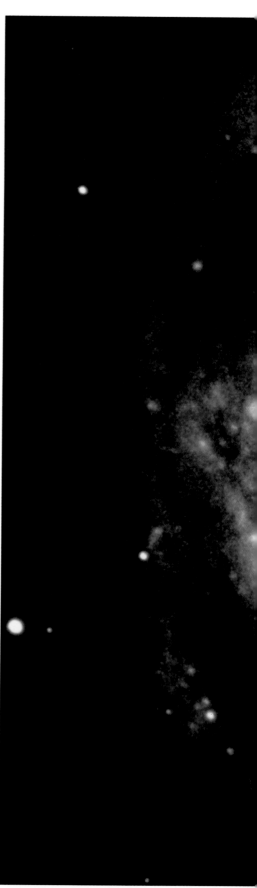

1. M51 (NGC 5195) RA 13h 30.0m Dec. +47° 16'

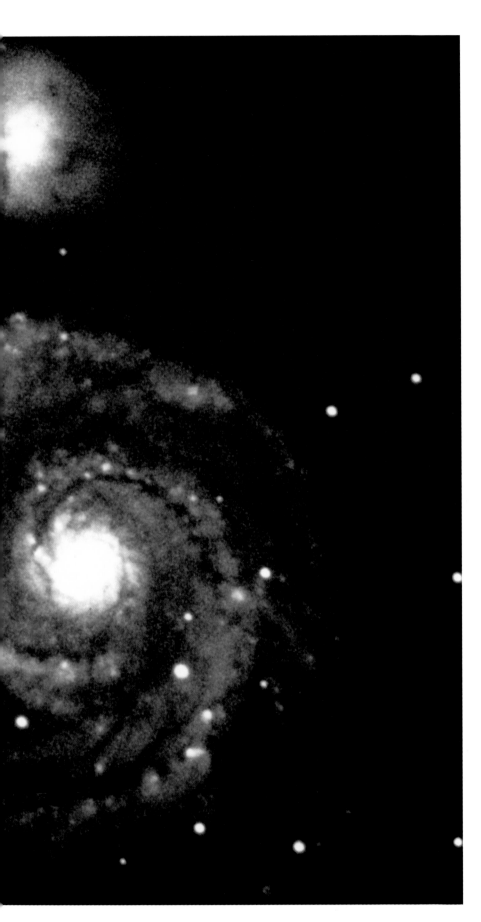

1.
THE "WHIRLPOOL" GALAXY IN CANES VENATICI, M51

M51 is a beautiful example of a spiral galaxy, seen from directly above, which shows the classic structure of the spiral arms after which this type of galaxy is named. Astronomers believe that our own galaxy has a very similar structure.

M51 is some 20 million light years away. At the top of the photograph is M51's companion; it is almost in contact with it and is classed as a "peculiar" spiral galaxy.

2. M88 RA 12h 32.0m Dec. +14° 25'

2.
A SPIRAL GALAXY IN COMA BERENICES, M88

Another spiral, this time seen at an angle of about 30 degrees to the plane of the galaxy. M88 is about 30 million light years away and was first observed in 1850 by Lord Rosse.

3. M104 RA 12h 40.0m Dec. −11° 37′

3.
THE "SOMBRERO" GALAXY IN VIRGO, M104

Although this object has an unusual appearance, M104 is actually a spiral galaxy, seen almost edge-on. The photograph shows clearly the "bulge" of the nucleus, and the dark rim is in fact composed of vast clouds, or "lanes", of dust that obscure light from the nucleus.

4.
GIANT ELLIPTICAL GALAXY IN VIRGO, M87

This extraordinary galaxy is shown in a photograph taken with the aid of a "charge-coupled device"; a piece of electronic equipment that allows very clear images to be produced and enhanced by computer, to show particular features of the subject.

In this case the "spike" coming from the centre is a jet of matter that is being ejected from the nucleus at high speed. The source of this jet is thought to be an enormous black hole, possibly as massive as 5000 million suns. Other extraordinary features of this galaxy include a halo of perhaps 4000 globular clusters (the Milky Way has only 100 or so) and a very strong source of radio waves that is another strong indication of a central black hole.

5.
"CENTAURUS A" RADIO GALAXY IN CENTAURUS, NGC 5128

Another massive source of radio emissions, this galaxy is some 16 million light years from Earth. The spectacular appearance of Centaurus A is caused by a great dust lane which obscures the centre of the galaxy. As with M87, astronomers are still trying to discover the source of the enormous energy output – possibly another giant black hole – of this enigmatic object.

4. M87 RA 12h 30.8m Dec. +12° 24′

5. NGC 5128 RA 13h 25.5m Dec. −43° 01′

STARCHART 6

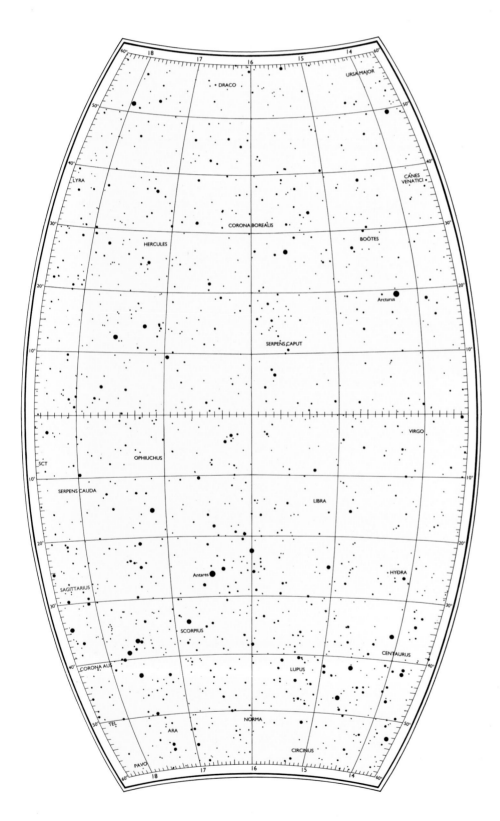

1. M13 RA 16h 41.7m Dec. +36° 28'

1.
THE "GREAT CLUSTER" IN HERCULES, M13

This object is a globular cluster, made up of perhaps half a million stars, at a distance of some 22,500 light years from Earth. All globular clusters are found in what is known as the "halo" – a great sphere surrounding the nucleus of our galaxy. Other similar galaxies also have halos around their nuclei.

Although M13 is only one of thousands of clusters in the galaxy, it is arguably one of the most beautiful objects in the sky. It was first identified by Sir Edmund Halley (of comet fame) in 1714 and is visible to the naked eye on a clear night. It is a wonderful sight through binoculars or a small telescope.

2.
TWO OPEN CLUSTERS IN SCORPIUS, M6 AND M7

These clusters are visible to the naked eye and are well worth observing with binoculars or telescope. M6 is about 1300 light years from Earth and occupies an area of space some 13 light years across. Because some of its stars have reached the orange giant stage of their lives it is thought that M6 is about 100 million years old.

M7 is closer at about 800 million light years and is some 20 light years across, and so it is visually much larger than M6 (which is about twice the size of a full moon). It is also thought to be older than M6 because it contains more orange stars.

2. M6 and M7 RA 17h 40.1m Dec. −32° 13′

3.
THE "EAGLE" NEBULA IN SERPENS
CAUDA, M16

A vast red cloud of hydrogen gas and
dust that shines because it is heated
by stars within the cloud. The nebula
is some 6000 light years away from
the Earth, and gets its name from the
eagle-shaped area of dark dust in the
centre of the nebula.

3. M16 RA 18h 18.8m Dec. − 13° 47′

4. M20 RA 18h 02.6m Dec. −23° 02′

4.
THE TRIFID NEBULA IN SAGITTARIUS, M20

This hauntingly beautiful nebula (also shown on Starchart 7) consists of a cloud of dust and gas, about 3000 light years from Earth. The Trifid itself is the pink area of hot gas in the lower half of the photograph; inside the area, you can see the stars that heat it, as well as the dark dust lanes that give it a curiously flower-like appearance.

In the blue cloud above the Trifid there is a small, bright star that is not heating the gas sufficiently to make it glow red. Instead the cloud shines with a blue light reflected by the dust particles within it.

5.
THE NORTH AMERICAN NEBULA IN CYGNUS, NGC 7000

The dense star fields of the Milky Way form a beautiful and striking background to this nebula, some 2300 light years from Earth. Discovered by noted astronomer Sir William Herschel in 1786, it was named for its curious and uncanny similarity in shape to that of the North American Continent.

6. M11 RA 18h 51.1m Dec. −06° 16′

6.
THE WILD DUCK CLUSTER IN SCUTUM, M11

This open cluster is a glorious example of a group containing both young blue stars and old red ones – more than 1000 in total, over 50 light years across.

5. NGC 7000 RA 20h 58.7m Dec. +44° 20′

STARCHART 7

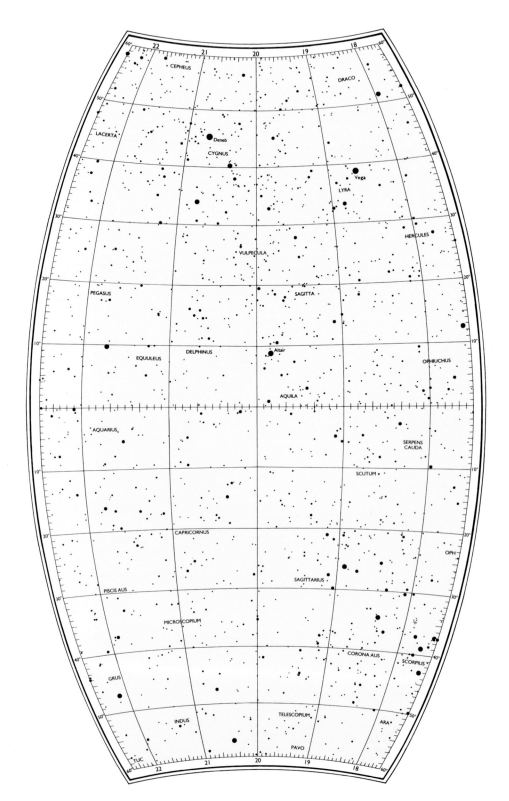

1.
THE "RING NEBULA" IN LYRA, M57

The "ring" is a planetary nebula and probably the most famous of its type. This expanding shell of gas is the result of a cataclysmic event when the central hot blue star, which can be seen in the photograph, ejected the material some 20,000 years ago. M57 is about 2000 light years from Earth and can just be seen through a small telescope.

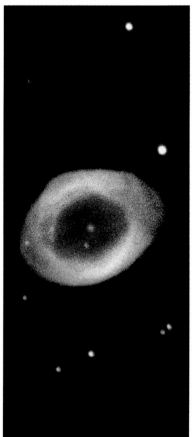

1. M57 RA 18h 53.6m Dec. +33° 02'

2.
THE "OMEGA" NEBULA, IN SAGITARIUS, M17

Also known as the "Horseshoe", this is an emission nebula like M8 and M20, overleaf. It is some 25 light years across and about 4800 light years from Earth.

2. M17 RA 18h 20.8m Dec. −16° 11′

3. M8 and M20 RA 18h 02.6m Dec. −23° 02′

3.
THE "LAGOON" AND "TRIFID" NEBULAE IN SAGITTARIUS, M8 & M20

Both these nebulae are giant clouds of gas and dust, and are examples of "emission" nebulae – so-called because they are heated by stars within the clouds and, as a result, emit light.

As with other nebulae, the red colour betrays the presence of hydrogen gas. One interesting feature of the Trifid is the nearby presence of a reflection nebulae - this can be seen as a small blue cloud just above the Trifid. The blue light is starlight reflected by the dust in the cloud; the star is not sufficiently hot to heat the gas enough to produce any other colour.

The Lagoon is about 50 light years across, and may contain enough material to form 1000 stars the size of the Sun. The clouds are about 4500 light years from Earth.

4.
A GLOBULAR CLUSTER IN SAGITTARIUS, M22

One of the finest globular clusters in the sky – and for southern observers it rivals even the great globular M13, in Hercules. No matter from where you view it, it is the easiest cluster in which to see individual stars. It is about 9600.light years away and 50 light years across, containing some half a million stars.

5.
THE "DUMB-BELL" NEBULA IN VULPECULA, M27

A planetary nebula, 50,000 years old, and expanding at some 17 miles (27km) per second. The cloud is about three light years in diameter, and you can just see the central star as a small blue dot.

4. M22 RA 18h 36.4m Dec. −23° 54′

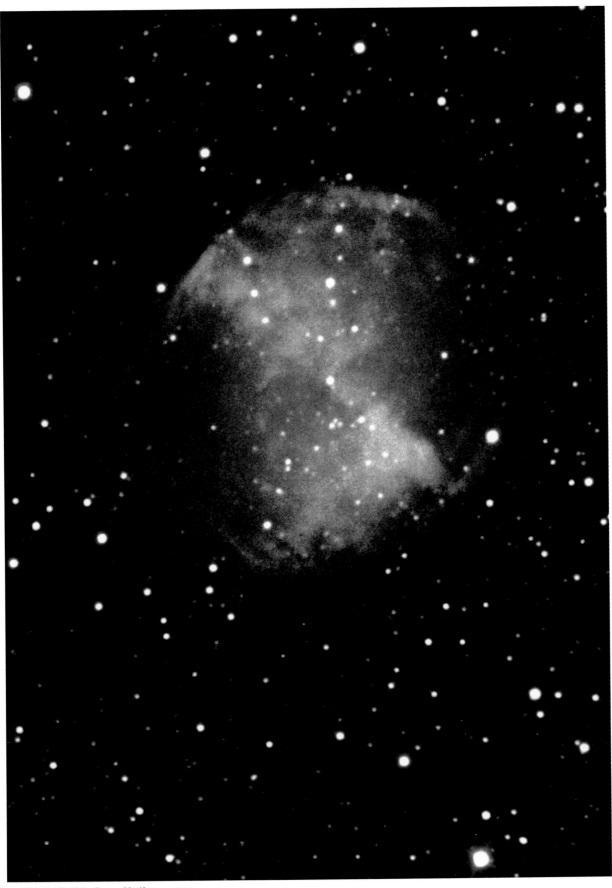

5. M27 RA 19h 59.6m Dec. +22° 43′

STARCHART 8

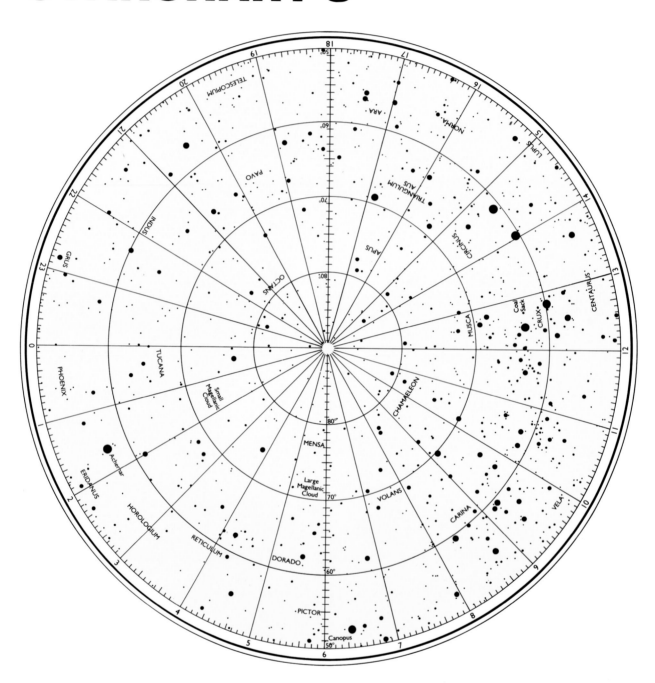

1.

THE SMALL MAGELLANIC CLOUD
IN TUCANA

Our galaxy, the Milky Way, has a number of companion galaxies, the most significant of which are the Small Magellanic Cloud (SMC) and the Large Magellanic Cloud (LMC). The SMC, seen here as an ill-defined misty patch looking rather like a faint

1. The Small Magellanic Cloud RA 01h 00m Dec. −73° 00'

2. The Large Magellanic Cloud RA 05h 20m Dec. −69° 00′

nebula, is some 195,000 light years outside the Milky Way.

The bright object just above the SMC is the globular cluster 47 Tucanae; inside our galaxy, this is the second largest and brightest cluster in the sky. Both the Large and Small Magellanic Clouds are named after the Portuguese navigator Ferdinand Magellan, whose crew reported them to the astronomers of Europe after his voyage round the world in 1519.

2.
THE LARGE MAGELLANIC CLOUD IN TUCANA

The largest of our companion galaxies, and the closest object outside the Milky Way, the LMC is about 180,000 light years away. The small pink area, just above the centre of the photograph, is the Tarantula nebula.

Very slightly below this is what appears to be just another relatively bright star. All the other stars are part of the Milky Way, but this one is actually inside the LMC and can be seen because it is a supernova (an exploding star), which was first observed in 1987 (*see below*).

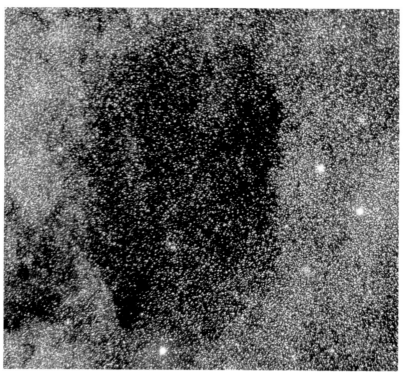

4. The Coalsack Nebula RA 12h 53.6m Dec. −60° 20'

3.
THE SUPERNOVA, 1987 A, IN THE LARGE MAGELLANIC CLOUD

This picture of the supernova is one of the earliest pictures to be taken by the Hubble Space Telescope and shows a ring of matter that is expanding away from the remnants of the star.

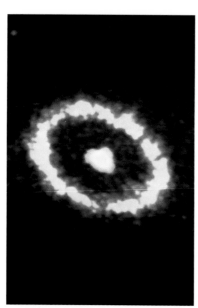

3. The Supernova, 1987 A (Hubble Space Telescope)

4.
THE COALSACK NEBULA IN CRUX AUSTRALIS

These beautiful star fields in the constellation of Crux Australis (the Southern Cross) have a dark, oval-shaped area. This is an example of a "dark" nebula, and is caused by a cloud of cold gas and dust that is obscuring the light shining from the stars beyond it.

5.
THE ETA CARINA NEBULA IN CARINA, NGC 3372

This vast area of hot gas is the remnant of a cloud that was once dark and cold. It has been heated over the last 2 million years by stars inside it, but the dust lanes that we see today are the remains of the original dark cloud.

The ETA Carina Nebula is about 300 light years across - that is some 20 times larger than the Great Nebula in Orion - and although it is some 9000 light years away it stretches across an area of the sky four times the width of the Moon.

5. NGC 3372 RA 10h 43.8m Dec. −59° 52'

NORTHERN SKY INDEX

● This chart shows all stars north of the celestial equator and is a combination of Starchart 1 and the top half of Charts 2 – 7. The dates around the edge show when the meridian through the pole and through the Right Ascension is overhead at midnight.

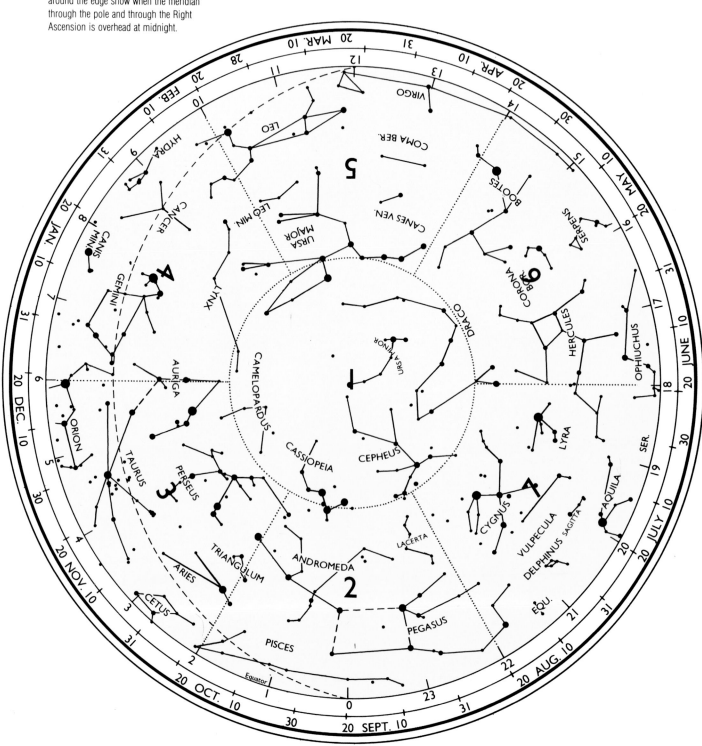

SOUTHERN SKY INDEX

● This chart shows all stars south of the celestial equator and is a combination of Starchart 1 and the bottom half of Charts 2 – 7. The dates around the edge show when the meridian through the pole and through the Right Ascension is overhead at midnight.

NORTHERN SKY CONSTELLATIONS

For reasons of clarity, the starcharts in this section do not show the boundaries of the constellations, just the stars. Use the charts on these pages to check which star belongs to which constellation.

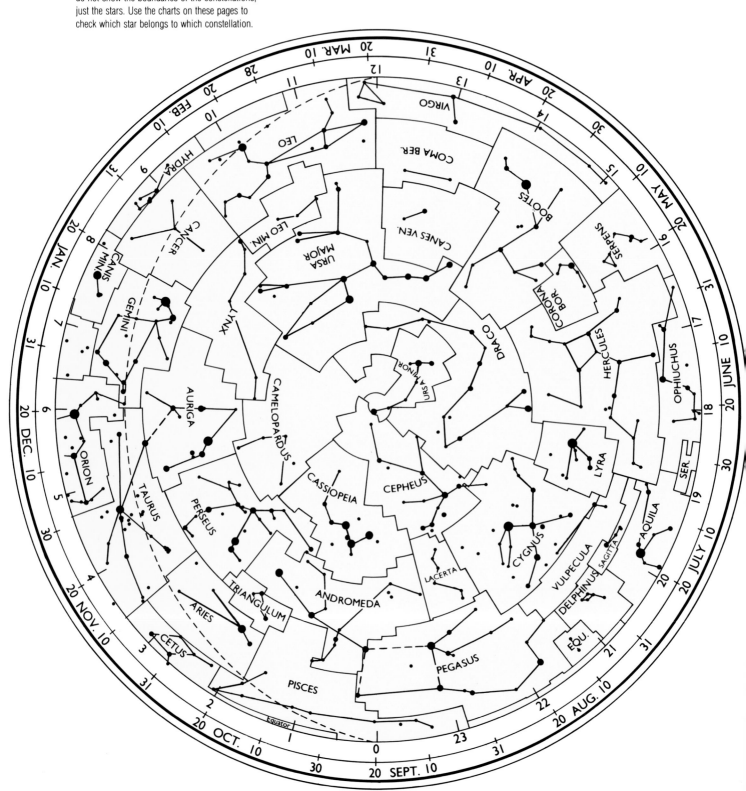

SOUTHERN SKY CONSTELLATIONS

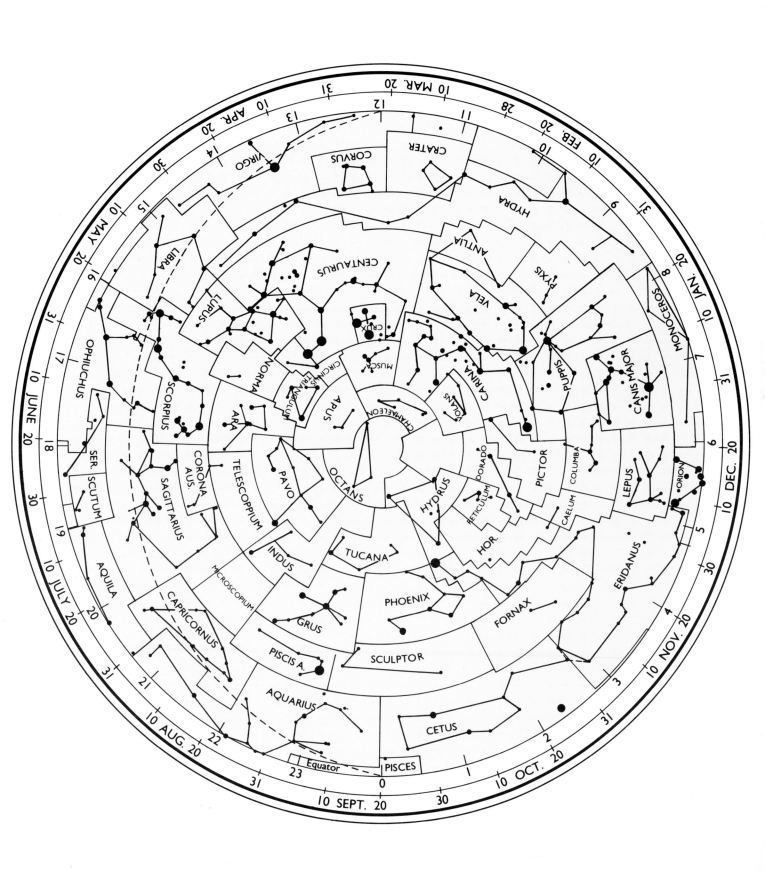

THE CONSTELLATIONS

Constellation	Known as	Chart	Constellation	Known as	Chart
Andromeda	Andromeda	2	Lacerta	The Lizard	2
Antilla	The Airpump	4,5	Leo	The Lion	4,5
Apus	The Bee	8	Leo Minor	The Little Lion	5
Aquarius	The Water-bearer	2,7	Lepus	The Hare	3
Aquilla	The Eagle	7	Libra	The Balance	6
Ara	The Altar	6,8	Lupus	The Wolf	6
Aries	The Ram	3	Lynx	The Lynx	1,4
Auriga	The Charioteer	3,4	Lyra	The Lyre	7
Bootes	The Herdsman	6	Mensa	The Table	8
Caelum	The Graving Tool	3	Microscopium	The Microscope	7
Camelopardalis	The Giraffe	1	Monocerus	The Unicorn	4
Cancer	The Crab	4	Musca Australis	The Southern Fly	8
Canes Venatici	The Hunting Dogs	5	Norma	The Rule	6
Canis Major	The Great Dog	4	Octans	The Octant	8
Canis Minor	The Little Dog	4	Ophicus	The Serpent-bearer	6
Capricornus	The Sea-Goat	7	Orion	The Hunter	3
Carina	The Keel	4,8	Pavo	The Peacock	8
Cassiopeia	Cassiopeia	1,2	Pegasus	The Winged Horse	2
Centaurus	The Centaur	5,8	Perseus	Perseus	3
Cepheus	Cepheus	1	Phoenix	The Phoenix	2
Cetus	The Whale	2,3	Pictor	The Painter	3,8
Chamaeleon	The Chameleon	8	Pisces	The Fishes	2
Circinus	The Compasses	8	Pisces Australis	The Southern Fishes	2
Columbia	The Dove	3	Puppis	The Poop	4
Coma Berenices	Berenice's Hair	5	Pyxis	The Mariner's Compass	4
Corona Australis	The Southern Crown	7	Reticulum	The Net	8
Corona Borealis	The Northern Crown	6	Sagitta	The Arrow	7
Corvus	The Crow	5	Sagittarius	The Archer	7
Crater	The Cup	5	Scorpius	The Scorpion	6
Crux Australis	The Southern Cross	8	Sculptor	The Sculptor	4
Cygnus	The Swan	7	Scutum	The Shield	7
Delphinus	The Dolphin	7	Serpens	The Serpent	6
Dorado	The Swordfish	8	Sextans	The Sextant	5
Draco	The Dragon	1	Taurus	The Bull	3
Equuleus	The Foal	7	Telescopium	The Telescope	7
Eridanus	The River	3	Triangulum	The Triangle	2
Fornax	The Furnace	3	Triangulum Australe	The Southern Triangle	8
Gemini	The Twins	4	Tucana	The Toucan	8
Grus	The Crane	2	Ursa Major	The Great Bear	1,5
Hercules	Hercules	6	Ursa Minor	The Little Bear	1
Horologium	The Clock	3,8	Vela	The Sails	4,5
Hydra	The Watersnake	4,5	Virgo	The Virgin	5
Hydrus	The Little Snake	8	Volans	The Flying Fish	8
Indus	The Indian	7,8	Vulpecula	The Fox	7

The constellations of the northern hemisphere, from *Harmonia Macrocosmica,* by Cellarius in 1660.

SECTION 3

PROBING SPACE AND TIME

SINCE THE EARLIEST DAYS of civilisation, astronomers have attempted to make sense of what can be seen in the stars. But for others the main aim has always been to understand how and why the universe came about. Today such people are called cosmologists.

Knowing what is out there in space is only the beginning of understanding how and why the universe is the way we see it today. With the advances that have been made in astronomy, particularly those of the 20th century, it is tempting to think that we are close to knowing most of what there is to know, and will soon be able to explain the origin of all things.

Unfortunately this is exactly what some do say, and have been saying for years. But theories come and go more quickly than the seasons, and it is a brave (or extremely optimistic) person who stands up and declares "I have all the answers".

When reading this book, you may have noticed the use of such words as "possibly", "perhaps" and even "probably", when describing the objects we see in the universe and our interpretation of their nature. If you decide to read other books on the subject you will certainly find that there are as many different interpretations of the theories that attempt to explain the universe as there are books (this is one of the few things that is certain in cosmology).

The reason for this usage is simple: astronomers, if they are being honest, have to admit that much of what they say is mere conjecture, and may well have to change as new discoveries are made. Even distances to, and sizes of, objects in space are often open to question. Because of this, it is important to all books such as this one as a guide, albeit one that is based on much scientific research, rather than the definitive article, whose contents can never be disputed.

In this section we look at some of the methods that astronomers use to unlock the mysteries of the universe; some of the more exotic objects they are attempting to explain; how we currently believe the universe has been evolving since its "creation"; and what its fate could be.

The section opens with a description of our main source of information about the skies: light, or, more correctly, electromagnetic radiation. This includes a look at how light can be affected by the motion of objects that emit it, and what this can tell us about the structure of the universe. The various components of the light we receive on Earth are studied by a wide variety of instruments and the most common of these are examined here, including not only the massive Earth-bound telescopes but some satellite-based instruments.

This section also looks at the way in which spaceflight has allowed us to investigate areas of astronomy that had previously been beyond our reach, because of the cloak of the Earth's atmosphere, and the possibilities and limitations for future exploration of the Solar System, the stars and the rest of the universe.

ABOVE This reflecting telescope, approximately 8 feet (2.5m) in diameter, inside the Mount Wilson Observatory, in America, is one of the instruments used by astronomers in their examination of space.

LEFT A cluster of galaxies far beyond the Milky Way, the pin-points of light are stars in our own galaxy.

Having described the nature of stars in Section 1 we now look in more detail at some of the more exotic objects that are found – or might be found – in space. This includes the evolution of objects from spectacular stellar explosions through to the ultimate collapse of matter to form an object so dense that not even light can escape: a black hole.

During recent years a number of new theories have been put forward to explain the origin of the universe and how the conditions prevailing then have affected the way in which the universe has evolved since. As with all new theories, there is great debate among cosmologists about the validity of this work, and no consensus has yet emerged – possibly because of the extremely complex mathematics on which these theories depend, and because very few people actually understand them.

Not surprisingly, then, the section does not even attempt to describe the very early universe but rather gives an overview of the most popular cosmological theory – the Big Bang – and what it means for the future evolution of the universe.

Finally, the section looks at the future of the Earth and humanity in space, explores the Solar System and travels the vast distances to the stars; finally speculating on whether we will ever meet beings from other worlds and civilisations.

THE ELECTROMAGNETIC SPECTRUM

WE ARE ALL FAMILIAR with the colours of the rainbow – red, orange, yellow, green, blue, indigo and violet – and in the 17th century Sir Isaac Newton showed that what we think of as "white" light is actually made up of all these colours. He shone a beam of light through a glass prism and saw that it was split up into a rainbow, or spectrum, of different colours.

To be correct, we should call this the "visible spectrum", because light is only one part of a much larger spectrum, which is called the "electromagnetic spectrum". To understand exactly what this is, you need to know a little more about the nature of light itself.

Light is a form of energy known as electromagnetic radiation. There are other forms of electromagnetic radiation, including radio waves, infra-red radiation, X-rays and gamma rays, the only difference between these types and visible light being in the amount of energy that each possesses.

Visible light is the form of electromagnatic radiation that we can detect with the naked eye. But this is not the only form of electromagnetic radiation that we use daily: we all use radio receivers to detect radio waves, and hospitals use X-rays to show such things as broken bones and details of joints.

Although these forms of radiation seem to be very different they are fundamentally the same. The various names we give this radiation are fairly arbitrary, being mainly for convenience, so that we know when we talk about X-rays, for example, that we are dealing with a type of radiation that has much more energy than radio waves – all are grouped together into what is known as the electromagnetic spectrum.

The schematic diagram of the electromagnetic spectrum shows the main areas into which electromagnetic radiation is grouped. The most "energetic" are the gamma rays, X-rays somewhat less so – and so on until we reach the lowest energy radiation that is radio waves. This is also true within the visible part of the spectrum – violet light, for example, has more light energy than red light.

In astronomy it is important to know what type of radiation, and hence what level of energy, is coming from a particular object in the sky, because this tells us a great deal about the nature of the object we are looking at. As a result, there are distinct areas of research in astronomy, each of which deals with one type of electromagnetic radiation, and that utilises its own type of equipment: X-ray astronomers use X-ray telescopes, for example; optical astronomers use telescopes that record visible light; radio astronomers use the giant dishes that are radio telescopes; and so on.

If a particular object is studied using different types of

Visible light is only a small part of the electromagnetic radiation that the Sun actually produces – the wavelength of the radiation decreases and its frequency increases from right to left in this diagram (the upper levels of Earth's atmosphere protects us from much of the harmful radiation to right and left of the visible spectrum). Astronomers can learn much about the nature of an object by measuring the amount and type of the radiation that it emits.

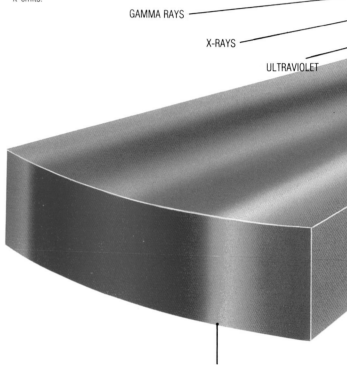

GAMMA RAYS

X-RAYS

ULTRAVIOLET

THE SPECTRUM OF VISIBLE LIGHT

telescope, the object can appear very ordinary in, for example, visible light but emit enormous amounts of radio waves when seen through a radio telescope. This immediately tells us that the object is very different from another one that looks the same, optically, but does not emit radio waves. In this way, more and more is being found out about the many types of object in the universe.

THE RED SHIFT

When light is emitted from an object it has a specific colour, in the case of visible light, that is characteristic of the elements – hydrogen, helium, and so on – that make up that object. So by looking at the spectrum of the light from stars and other bodies in the sky, we can work out their composition.

There are, however, ways in which the initial colour of the light can be changed before it reaches us. The first of these is gravity – when light travels out of a gravitational field it loses energy. As the colour of light is related to its

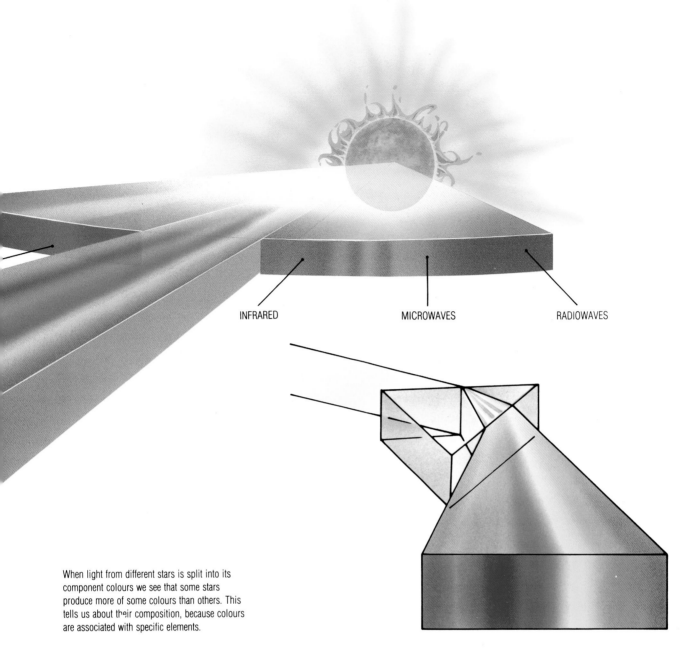

INFRARED   MICROWAVES   RADIOWAVES

When light from different stars is split into its component colours we see that some stars produce more of some colours than others. This tells us about their composition, because colours are associated with specific elements.

energy this means that, as light loses energy, it changes colour – it moves towards the red end of the visible part of the electromagnetic spectrum.

Another cause of colour change is the movement of the source that emits the light. If an object is moving away from us then its light is "stretched" and its energy is reduced, causing it to look redder than it originally did.

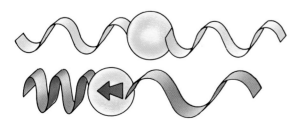

If an object is stationary relative to Earth we can see its true colour, but if it is moving towards us its light is "squashed" and appears more blue than normal. If it is moving away, the light is "stretched" and appears more red, or "red shifted".

This process also works in reverse – if an object is moving towards us, its light is "squashed" and the light appears bluer than it was.

The importance of the red shift is that the amount by which light is "shifted" is directly related to the speed at which an object is moving away from us. This means that we can look at the colour of objects all over the sky and find out how the universe is moving around us.

HUBBLE'S LAW

One particularly useful application of the red shift was identified by Sir Edwin Hubble, in 1929. He showed that for objects outside our galaxy, red shifts are directly related to how far an object is away from us.

This had important implications for astronomers and cosmologists, because it provided a simple method for discovering the distance of remote objects, and therefore a better idea of the size of the universe.

THE STUDY OF SPACE — MODERN METHODS

TELESCOPES

NEARLY ALL THE INFORMATION scientists have about the universe comes through the study of electromagnetic radiation. Looking at the sky through a normal optical telescope is fascinating, but what can be seen often appears as nothing more than a point of light or a misty cloud. In practice, astronomers hardly ever "look" through a telescope – instead, they rely on detailed examination of long-exposure photographs taken through the telescopes, because these show much more detail than they would pick out themselves.

Nevertheless, both optical and radio telescopes still have their uses, and play their part in increasing our understanding of the universe.

Even such photographs, though, do not tell astronomers everything that they want to know. Because of this, scientists have developed various different pieces of equipment that can count how much radiation comes from an object, split light into its component colours, analyse the composition of stars, and so on.

OPTICAL TELESCOPES

As described in Section 2, two main types of telescope are used for studying visible light: the reflector and the refractor. They are both basically simple. The reflector telescopes collects incoming light by means of a large "main", or "primary", mirror that reflects light to a point at which it can be seen through an eyepiece. The refractor telescope focuses the light through a main, or "object", lens into an eyepiece – refer to the various diagrams on pages 72 and 73 to see how this works.

One of the greatest problems astronomers face is to get enough light to be able to examine objects in sufficient detail. Refractor telescopes have one particular disadvantage in that some of the incoming light is reflected away by the glass of the object lens and is lost. Although a reflector telescope has a lower magnification than a refractor, it collects more light than it. As a result, the majority of large telescopes work on the reflector principle. The largest reflecting telescopes have primary mirrors with diameters of the order of 3.25 yards (3m).

Another problem with Earth-based telescopes is that the light from astronomical bodies travels through our atmosphere, and the apparent position of a star, or other object, is changed because its light is bent, or "refracted", as it does so. This light is also scattered by particles in the atmosphere, so some is lost. Light from Earth is scattered, too, making faint stars more difficult to see. In order to reduce these effects as much as possible, most research telescopes are placed in high locations – on mountain tops, for example. This reduces the amount of atmosphere through which starlight has to pass and increases the amount of light received.

RADIO TELESCOPES

Fortunately for the radio astronomer, the Earth's atmosphere is virtually transparent to radio waves. As a result, radio telescopes can be placed wherever is most convenient. A radio telescope is effectively a directional radio aerial, which receives the same type of signal as our conventional radio sets at home, but which has to be able to point with great accuracy.

The most common type of radio telescope is the giant dish, which can be 100 yards (90m) or more in diameter. Some of these can be aimed in any direction but many instruments are designed so that they can only move in altitude (up and down) and use the Earth's rotation to provide their movement around (side to side) the sky.

There is one particularly spectacular instrument at Arecibo, in Puerto Rico, that is about 325 yards (300m) in diameter. The telescope is not a man-made dish but a

LEFT The dome of the Mount Palomar Observatory, in California.

BELOW The 200-inch (5m) telescope of the Mount Palomar Observatory.

Some of the 27 radio dishes that make up the world's largest radio interferometer – the Very Large Array, in New Mexico.

The world's largest single radio telescope, 1000 feet (300m) in diameter, built into a natural crater in Arecibo, Puerto Rico.

natural crater that has been lined with mesh and is, of course, fixed in position. However, it can be aimed by changing the position of the central aerial that hangs above the crater at the main focus of the telescope.

Unlike optical telescopes, radio telescopes can be connected together to form what is called an interferometer. This is an array of individual radio dishes, linked together so that they act as one giant instrument. One of these, the Very Large Array, in New Mexico, combines 27 separate dishes to form one massive instrument that is effectively 15 miles (25km) in diameter. This technique is now being extended to combine signals from dishes across continents, so it should theoretically be possible one day to launch several radio telescopes into space to form a single enormous interferometer.

SPACE TELESCOPES

The effect of the Earth's atmosphere on optical telescopes is most evident on a cloudy night – nothing can be seen at all. But when it comes to detecting any type of radiation – other than visible light and radio waves – the sky is always "cloudy". This is because the atmosphere absorbs the radiation, so we cannot detect it without going above the atmosphere – into Earth's orbit. (In the case of infra-red radiation, the problem can be overcome to a certain extent by placing telescopes on mountain tops, but the results are not entirely satisfactory.)

Some results can be achieved by means of temporary telescopes carried by high-altitude balloons and small rockets, but these return to Earth after a short period, so do not help when it comes to extended studies of the sky.

The only long-term approach to the problem is to place a satellite into orbit around the Earth, in such a position that it will stay in place indefinitely as a platform for observations. The minimum height for an orbit in which the drag of the atmosphere has no real effect is about 100 miles (160km), and at this the satellite will complete an orbit of the Earth in 88 minutes. The effect of gravity, which pulls the satellite back to Earth, decreases with height so there is a correct speed for every height. Typically, for a height of 300 miles (500km), the satellite must travel at about 19,000 mph (30,000 kmph); slower than this the satellite will fall back to Earth; faster and it will go into an elliptical orbit.

Larger artificial satellites can be seen with the naked eye and look like stars, but ones that move slowly against the background. Details of the times at which they can be seen are often published in daily newspapers.

The first satellite to be successfully launched into Earth orbit was the Russian Sputnik 1, on October 4, 1957. This did little more than go "bleep", but it was the first step to an essential part of our communications network and scientific research programme.

In 1958 the first American satellite, Explorer 1, discovered that there are areas of intense radiation around the Earth. These are now called the Van Allen belts, and are caused by charged particles from the Sun that are trapped in the Earth's magnetic field. At times when there is a great deal of activity on the Sun, associated with Solar Flares, the number of charged particles sent out is greatly increased and these cannot be contained in the Van Allen belts. The result is that they shower down into the atmosphere, towards the Earth's magnetic poles, and cause the glowing curtains of light called aurorae. These outbursts from the Sun cause electrical storms that can severely disrupt communications on Earth.
Modern astronomical studies have generally been concerned with the invisible areas of the electromagnetic spectrum, the most notable of them being the International Ultraviolet Explorer (IUE), the Infrared Astronomical Satellite (IRAS) and the X-ray telescope

The Hubble Space Telescope during deployment from the space shuttle Discovery on April 24, 1990. This instrument was designed to look seven times further into the universe than ever before.

mounted on the HEA0-2 satellite, now renamed Einstein.

One of the most recent additions to this family of artificial moons is the long-awaited Hubble Space Telescope (HST). On April 24, 1990, America's space shuttle, *Discovery*, carried Hubble into orbit. The shuttle flew higher than any previous mission, some 375 miles (600km) above the Earth's surface. The exciting thing about this particular satellite is that is will be used not just for one area of astronomy, but incorporates a wide range of equipment that is intended to carry through 467 individual projects in the first year alone.

Apart from this range and number of observations, Hubble should be capable of seeing more clearly and further into the universe than any other telescope. The experiments take in all aspects of astronomy, from mapping the surface of Mars to studying distant quasars and investigating the origin of the universe itself. Perhaps one of its most appropriate tasks is that of measuring distances to other galaxies – the research for which Sir Edwin Hubble, after whom the Hubble Space Telescope is named, is renowned.

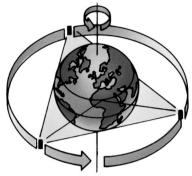

ABOVE Satellites can be placed into orbits anything from a few hundred to many thousands of miles above Earth. Some maintain their position above a specific point on the surface – a geostationary orbit – while others circle the Earth many times a day.

ABOVE The International Ultraviolet Explorer (IUE) satellite, which was launched in 1978, under construction at the Goddard Space Flight Centre, Maryland.

LEFT A model of IRAS, the Infrared Astronomical Satellite, which was launched in 1983 into an orbit 560 miles (900km) above Earth. Its all-sky survey of infrared sources has recently been the basis for work on the large-scale structure of the universe.

EXPLORING THE SOLAR SYSTEM

The Chinese were adept at building rockets thousands of years ago, but these were not much more than fireworks, using simple powder as fuel. Nevertheless, the principles involved in those simple projectiles were the same as those that are employed today to send spacecraft high above the Earth and land men on the Moon.

One of the problems of building a rocket capable of reaching escape velocity, and maintaining it sufficiently long to reach Earth orbit, was to find a fuel that would provide the vast energy required for such a feat. Today we are familiar with the giant tanks of liquid oxygen that are used to power conventional rocket boosters. But this all began with the historic launch of the first liquid propelled rocket ever to fly, on March 16, 1926. This tiny predecessor to the modern giants was built and launched by Robert Goddard, from the farm belonging to his Aunt Effie, in Massachusetts, USA. Its momentous voyage lasted two and a half seconds.

Traditional rockets, such as the sky-scraper sized Saturn V that launched Apollo missions to the Moon, presented numerous disadvantages. They were one-time-only boosters that ended up, variously, as junk at the bottom of the ocean and orbiting debris that was rapidly filling up the sky and causing not inconsiderable traffic problems. These "disposable" rockets were expensive and the space vehicle on the top had little control over where it went, other than to make minor corrections to a pre-planned route.

The advent of the American space shuttle hailed the beginning of a new era in spaceflight. Not only was this vehicle reuseable but it could carry large payloads, such as satellites, and manoeuvre in space unlike any previous craft. It could also recover damaged or malfunctioning satellites, either for return to Earth or in-flight repairs. The ability to perform frequent missions, and the flexibility to move freely in space, at last meant that humans could actually use Earth-orbit as a workplace rather than just visit it as a tourist.

But manned spacecraft still represent enormous logistical problems, because of the need to provide an environment in which human beings can survive. For the present, at least, exploration of the Solar System must remain in the mechanical hands of robot space probes, and less than half a century after the first primitive artificial satellite was launched there are now distant spacecraft heading out beyond the orbits of the planets, billions of miles from Earth.

Since its launch on August 20, 1977, the Voyager 2

Indeed, it was less than four hundred years ago that Galileo first noticed that any of the planets, other than Earth, had moons of their own. During the billions of years of Earth's history, nothing much ever got off the ground, except for a few birds. Now, in less than 50 years, we are surrounded by swarms of artificial satellites, most of which no longer work; there are dozens of spacecraft going here, there and everywhere; Voyagers have even reached the outermost planets and are wandering off into the Galaxy, never to return.

So, is there any more to discover about the Solar System, or shall we all forget about it? Well, considering that most astronomers will agree that they don't even know where our closest neighbour, the Moon, came from, it would seem that there is still a great deal to do. It may seem that there is already a bewildering amount of information about the planets, but, with every new piece of information, we realise that we are getting new questions far faster than we are producing answers – there doesn't appear to be any shortage of work for planetary astronomers for some time to come.

ABOVE Robert Goddard with the first liquid-propelled rocket, in 1926.

LEFT Apollo 11's Lunar Excursion Module, the section of the spacecraft that landed on the Moon's surface, seen from the Command Module with Earth rising in the background.

spacecraft has travelled through the Solar System sending back pictures and data from the planets, showing us wholly unexpected alien landscapes on the moons of some of these worlds. Its "grand tour" of the Solar System began with an arcing fly-past of Mars whose gravitational field swung the ship out through the asteroid belt. Far into the depths between the outer planets the light of the Sun is too weak to provide power by means of solar cells so Voyager's instruments are driven by a tiny nuclear reactor, providing its energy from a small core pellet of plutonium. There are no giant rockets to steer the craft from one encounter to the next – all of Voyager's journey is governed by the gravitational pull of the planets, its course past Jupiter accelerated it and swept it round toward Saturn. From there it sped on to the twin planets of Uranus and Neptune, its last port of call before heading out into the vast interstellar reaches, travelling now for tens of thousands of years without encountering the light and warmth of another star system.

For the better part of 5 thousand million years the Sun has been shining on the face of the planets and their moons. But for almost all of that time nobody had seen anything more of them than a few bright lights in the sky.

The Magellan spacecraft being deployed prior to its voyage to Venus.

MOTION OF STARS

THE MODERN TECHNIQUES used to study space, described on the previous pages, have given us an enormous amount more information than early astronomers had at their disposal. But although they were wrong to think that the Earth was at the centre of the universe, they were correct in their assumption that the stars remained in the same relative position in the sky.

But if astronomers could look at the sky at intervals of millions of years, would the stars look the same? Of course, some would have evolved into red giants, or white dwarfs, or even have exploded. But these would be few in relation to the vast majority, for which a million years is just the blink of an eye.

The stars are not as "fixed" as we might think, though. They are all in motion, in various directions, and it is only the great distance between them that causes us to miss their movement. Their motion has a number of different components. All the stars in the disk of the Galaxy are rotating around its nucleus, although at different speeds; those near the centre are moving faster than those towards the edge. The Sun, for example, is whizzing around the Galaxy at about 250 miles (400km) per second, but even at this speed it takes about 250 million years to complete one circuit.

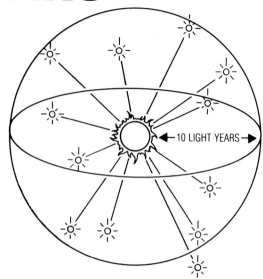

The great distances between the stars – there are only 11 within 10 light years of the Sun – mean that the proper motion of an individual star can pass unnoticed, even over centuries of time.

Apart from their rotation around the nucleus of the Galaxy, stars also have their individual motions, wandering separately in their courses. The Sun, for example, is winging its way towards a point in the constellation of Hercules, at a few tens of miles per

*Nearest and **Brightest Stars***

THE NEAREST STARS		
	Star	Distance l.y.
1	*Proxima* Cen	4·3
2	α Cen A	4·3
3	α Cen B	4·3
4	Barnard's star	6·0
5	Wolf 359	8·1
6	Lal 21185	8·2
7	*Sirius* A	8·7
8	*Sirius* B	8·7
9	UV Cet A	9·0
10	UV Cet B	9·0
11	Ross 154	9·3
12	Ross 248	10·3
13	ε Eri	10·8
14	L 789-6	11·1
15	Ross 128	11·1
16	61 Cyg A	11·2
17	61 Cyg B	11·2
18	*Procyon A*	11·3
19	*Procyon B*	11·3
20	ε Ind	11·4
21	Σ 2398 A	11·6
22	Σ 2398 B	11·6
23	Grb 34 A	11·7
24	Grb 34 B	11·7
25	Lac 9352	11·9

THE BRIGHTEST STARS			
	Star	Proper name	Distance l.y.
1	α CMa	*Sirius*	8·7
2	α Car	*Canopus*	180
3	α Cen	*Rigil Kent*	4.3
4	α Boo	*Arcturus*	36
5	α Lyr	*Vega*	26
6	β Ori	*Rigel*	815
7	α Aur	*Capella* (binary)	45
8	α CMi	*Procyon*	11
9	α Eri	*Achernar*	142
10	β Cen	*Hadar*	400
11	α Aql	*Altair*	16
12	α Tao	*Aldebaran*	68
13	α Cru	*Acrux*	270
14	α Ori	*Belelgeuse (var.)*	650
15	α Sco	*Antares*	400
16	α Vir	*Spica*	270
17	β Gem	*Pollux*	35
18	α PsA	*Fomalhaut*	23
19	α Cyg	*Deneb*	1600
20	β Cru	*Mimosa*	460
21	α Leo	*Regulus*	85
22	ε CMa	*Adhara*	650
23	γ Ori	*Bellatrix*	300
24	λ Sco	*Shaula*	300
25	β Tau	*El Nath*	180

second. Although there appear to be some trends for the direction of motion of the stars, the overall effect is that they do not keep their relative position in the sky. This means that over long periods of time the constellations change their shape in the sky.

As early as 1718, Sir Edmund Halley noticed that the positions of some stars were substantially different to those given by early Greek astronomers. He suggested that these stars had indeed moved, and that the difference in position could not be put down to observational error.

The motion of stars in space is both transverse (left, right, up or down) and radial (away from, or towards us). The radial motion has no effect on the observed position of a star, but transverse motion can be seen, especially in the case of the nearer stars, whose change in position will be relatively greater than distant ones.

The transverse component of a star's movement is called proper motion – its effect on the stars in the Plough, in the constellation of Ursa Major, is shown in the diagram here. Five of the stars are travelling roughly together, but the other two are going in almost the opposite direction.

This demonstrates that the stars in the Plough are not in fact related, as is the case in some clusters, such as the Pleiades. There may appear to be some mutual relationship between the stars of a number of groups, but generally this is only a line-of-sight effect.

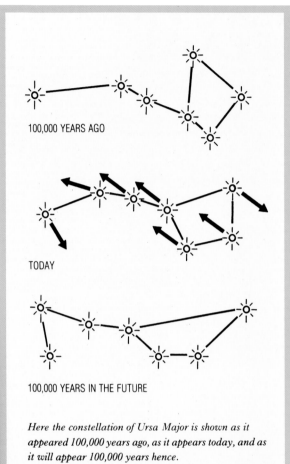

100,000 YEARS AGO

TODAY

100,000 YEARS IN THE FUTURE

Here the constellation of Ursa Major is shown as it appeared 100,000 years ago, as it appears today, and as it will appear 100,000 years hence.

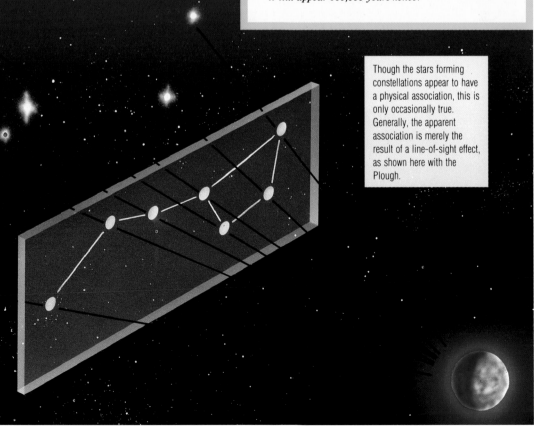

Though the stars forming constellations appear to have a physical association, this is only occasionally true. Generally, the apparent association is merely the result of a line-of-sight effect, as shown here with the Plough.

EXOTIC STARS

HOW STARS EVOLVE has been explained in Section One, as has the fact that material is left behind when a star explodes and subsequently collapses. But what exactly happens to this material depends on the mass of the star – the more massive it is, the more awe-inspiring the result. All the objects described here are stellar remnants: some fade into insignificance; others turn into one of the most extraordinary entities in the universe – a black hole.

WHITE DWARFS

A star similar in size to the Sun will expand in the later stages of its evolution, as matter is used up, and will become a red giant. Eventually it will become unstable and eject the outer layers of its atmosphere into space, leaving only its core, which has no further means of generating energy: the star will have become a white dwarf, radiating its heat away into space.

Because there is no outward radiation the star's own gravitational field causes it to shrink until it eventually collapses to a point where all its atoms are squeezed together with no space in between them.

The matter in such a body is very much more dense than anything with which we are familiar on Earth. Some white dwarfs have a total mass greater than that of the Sun but are only a few thousand miles across – a matchbox full of the material of which they are composed would weigh hundreds of tonnes.

Such stars are common in the Galaxy, but they are small and faint – as they lose the last of their heat they cool, and eventually become too dim to be seen, until they end up as black dwarfs.

NEUTRON STARS

For stars more massive than the Sun (about one and a half times) the gravitational collapse at the end of their lives is far more dramatic than that of a white dwarf.

Inside a white dwarf, atoms are squeezed together to form a very dense object – they behave rather like a miniature Solar System, with a relatively massive nucleus at their centre and a number of minute electrons orbiting that nucleus, just as the planets orbit the Sun. As in the Solar System, there is a great deal of empty space inside an atom, and some of this empty space stays intact when a star collapses to form a white dwarf.

But when heavier stars collapse, their gravitational field is so great that the electrons inside their atoms are crushed into the nucleus, just as if the planets had been

This illustration shows approximate relative sizes of a black hole, neutron star, white dwarf, compared to a star such as the Sun.

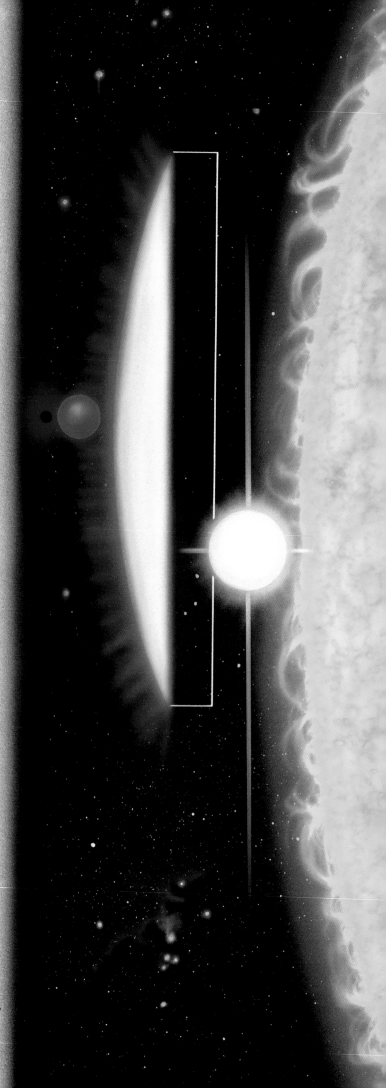

rotating neutron stars that are emitting a beam of radiation. As the star rotates, its beam sweeps past the Earth on each rotation, the result being a pulse of radio waves – but not, disappointedly, other life forms.

Probably the best known example of a pulsar is the neutron star that remains after the supernova explosion noted by Chinese astronomers in 1054, whose remnants can now be seen as a cloud of expanding gas – this is known as the Crab Nebula. This pulsar rotates some thirty times a second; the rotation is believed to be as fast as this because it is the result of a relatively recent explosion, whereas other pulsars are much older and have slowed down with age.

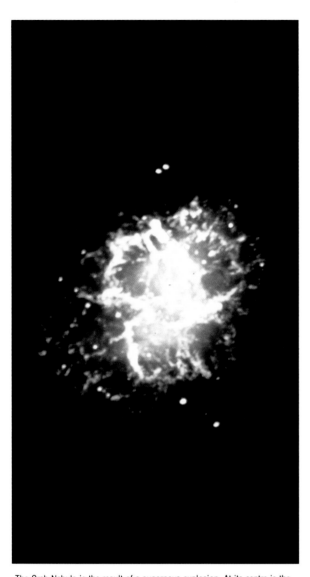

The Crab Nebula is the result of a supernova explosion. At its centre is the remnant of the original star that has collapsed to form a pulsar.

pulled into the Sun by its gravitational field. The result is an almost unimaginably dense object known as a neutron star. Typically, a neutron star will have all its mass compressed into a sphere that might be only 10 miles (16km) in diameter and our now greatly overburdened matchboxful would weigh hundreds of millions of tons.

PULSARS

In 1967 a researcher at Cambridge University detected a number of objects that were emitting radio waves. This was nothing unusual – many objects in the sky emit radio waves. But these were different: the radio pulses were extremely regular, every second or so.

For a while there was great excitement, as it was thought that these transmissions might be caused by some extra-terrestrial civilisation trying to contact us. The explanation turned out to be rather different: the objects, since named pulsars, are now thought to be rapidly

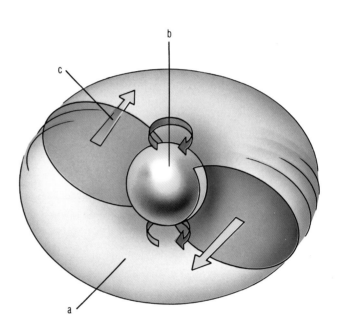

Strong magnetic fields (a) around rapidly rotating neutron stars (b) create intense radio beams (c) that cause a lighthouse effect. Astronomers call these types of stars pulsars.

BLACK HOLES

The objects described above may stretch the imagination, and, possibly, your credibility, to its limits, but if you are to accept the existence of black holes then you must cast aside most of what you would normally consider to be common sense.

The idea that black holes might exist is not new, however, for as early as 1783 a Cambridge University lecturer suggested their existence. But it was not until early in the 20th century that black holes could be described in terms of mathematics, with the help of the general theory of relativity, proposed by the physicist Albert Einstein in 1915.

Before we look at the startling nature of a black hole itself, it is useful to describe the process by which it is formed. In that most spectacular of events, a supernova, a large star ejects a great deal of its matter in a massive explosion. At this time the entire body of the star can be destroyed, leaving only an expanding cloud of gas. But if the core of the star remains intact there are two possibilities: if the star has a relatively low mass, the core will collapse to form a neutron star, as described above; when its mass is larger, the gravitational field is so intense that the matter of which it is composed is crushed – apparently out of existence!

This last statement implies that the remnant of the supernova is completely destroyed by its own gravitational collapse. In fact, though, this is only true in as much as the object shrinks to zero size – that is, the star's diameter is zero. But the gravitational field of the remnant still remains, and gravity can only exist in the presence of matter. The incredible implication is that the matter still exists but in an object that has no size – its density, therefore, must be infinite! Such an object is known, appropriately, as a "singularity". But this singularity is not, in itself, what is known as a black hole. The space around the singularity takes on peculiar characteristics, and to understand these it is helpful to explain them in terms of the Earth's gravitational field.

We are all familiar with the phrase "what goes up must come down", and if a ball is thrown into the air it does indeed come down again. But if you throw the ball fast enough it will continue upwards until it escapes from Earth's gravity, never to return – the speed that you need to achieve this is called the escape velocity; in the case of the Earth's gravitational field this is about 7 miles per second (11kmps). Naturally, on a more massive planet, which has a stronger gravitational field, the escape velocity will be higher.

But what has all this ball-throwing got to do with black holes? The answer lies in the escape velocity of the singularity. The intensity of the gravitational field, and hence the escape velocity, of an object depends on the mass of that object and the volume in which that mass is contained – its density. In the case of a singularity the density is so great that the escape velocity in the area of space around it is either equal to, or greater than, the speed of light.

But Einstein's Theory of Relativity shows that nothing can travel at a speed equal to, or faster than, the speed of light. So it is impossible for anything to leave the space around a singularity in which the escape velocity is equal to, or greater than, the speed of light. This, in turn, means that not even light can escape from the area around the singularity, and so this volume of space is said to be a black hole. As is the case with any type of hole, though, a black hole has an edge. Because the intensity of gravity decreases with distance from the singularity, there is a radius at which the escape velocity is exactly equal to the speed of light. This is the radius of the volume of space from which light cannot escape, and is called the "event horizon" – no event inside this boundary can ever be

detected in the universe outside it.

To sum up: a black hole is caused by the total collapse of a star, under the force of its own gravity, to form a singularity. Around the singularity is an area of space, bounded by the event horizon; inside this the escape velocity is greater than the speed of light, and it is this area that we call a black hole. Anything, including light, that falls into a black hole is lost forever.

But if we cannot "see" black holes, how do we know they exist? Well, in practice, we don't. Theory predicts that there must be black holes, but there is no way of detecting them directly. However, though we cannot actually look at a black hole, there is still the gravitational pull of the star from which it formed, and this will have an effect on nearby objects, such as other stars. To explain this we need to look at the way in which some stars stick together in twos, threes or multiple systems.

Our Sun is a solitary individual, sitting alone in space, light years away from its nearest neighbours. Many stars, however, formed in clouds of gas very close to other stars. Because of their mutual gravitational attraction, they stay together and orbit around their common centre of gravity. Such stars can be as close together as a few tens of millions of miles, and, being relatively so close, they can have considerable effects on each other, and even transfer matter from one to another.

The importance of these two-star system stars in detecting black holes is that in some cases the second star is a black hole. If a star is seen to be moving in the way that we expect two-star systems to behave, but the second star cannot be seen, then there is a good chance that the "second star" is, in fact, a black hole. And, indeed, a number of stars do seem to "wobble", but they have no visible companions.

One consequence of the existence of a black hole in association with a star, is that matter may be sucked off the visible star and swallowed by the black hole. When this happens, the matter swirls around in the black hole's gravitational field and is accelerated almost to the speed of light, to form what is called an accretion disk. The rapid motion causes a great deal of intense radiation to be generated at the inner edge of the accretion disk, just before the matter falls inside the event horizon and disappears forever.

So the combination of a "wobbling" star that has no apparent partner and an intense source of radiation in the same area is a good indication of the presence of a black hole – and it is significant that a number of such combinations have been observed.

The only hope we have of actually detecting a black hole is through its effect on neighbouring objects. If a black hole should happen to be part of a close double star system, then we might be able to observe vast amounts of energy being generated by an otherwise empty region of space, as matter from the companion star is dragged into an accretion disk around the event horizon of the black hole.

GALAXIES AND QUASARS

OUR OWN GALAXY, the Milky Way, has a spiral structure made up of billions of stars, as has been described. This type of shape is common to most large galaxies and consists of three main components: the central bulge of the nucleus; the disc that contains the spiral arms (from which this type of galaxy derives its name); and the halo in which we can see the globular clusters and some very ancient stars that have reached the later stages of their lives and are now dwarfs.

There are various different shapes of galaxy and astronomers have a detailed system of classification for their structure; however, all fall into four main types:

ELLIPTICAL GALAXIES

These range from nearly spherical to almost cigar-shaped, and have enormous differences in the numbers of stars and their sizes; dwarf ellipticals may contain only a few million stars and have a diameter of a few thousand light years; giant ellipticals can contain thousands of billions of stars and be far larger than our own galaxy.

NORMAL SPIRAL GALAXIES

Although the structure of spirals makes them look as if the arms are the result of some process of "winding up" as the galaxy rotates, this is not the case. The arms have existed for billions of years, and stars nearer the nucleus orbit the galaxy faster than those near the edges, so the arms cannot be lasting structures but are more akin to ripples in a rotating whirlpool. Spirals are classified by the extent of openness of their arms and the size of the central nucleus.

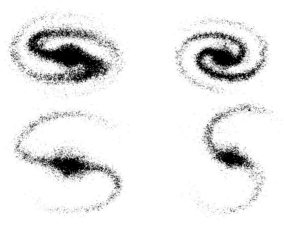

BARRED SPIRAL GALAXIES

These are similar in structure to the more open spiral galaxies, but have a bar on either side of the nucleus, in which the spiral arms originate. Roughly one third of all spirals are barred, and these are classified in a similar way to normal spiral galaxies.

IRREGULAR GALAXIES

As the name suggests, these are galaxies that have no particular identifiable structure. They tend to be small satellites of other larger galaxies, such as the Magellanic Clouds that orbit the Milky Way. It is thought that their irregular shape is caused by the gravitational disruption of their larger companions.

OTHER GALACTIC TYPES

The majority of galaxies do not exhibit any unusual characteristics and appear to be in long-term equilibrium. Some, however, emit far more energy than might be expected, and others even appear to have exploding nuclei. These are often called active galaxies; it appears that they generate great energies in all areas of the electromagnetic spectrum, but particularly in the radio and visible wavelengths.

It is frequently the nuclei of these galaxies that appear to be the source of this energy emission. However, it is difficult to explain the process by which the amount of energy can be generated, and why the energy emission varies so erratically.

Some scientists have suggested that giant black holes may have formed in the nuclei of these galaxies, and that these are sucking in vast quantities of material, while others believe that frequent supernovae explosions account for the energy output.

In practice, no single solution seems to explain satisfactorily the different varieties of behaviour observed in these peculiar objects.

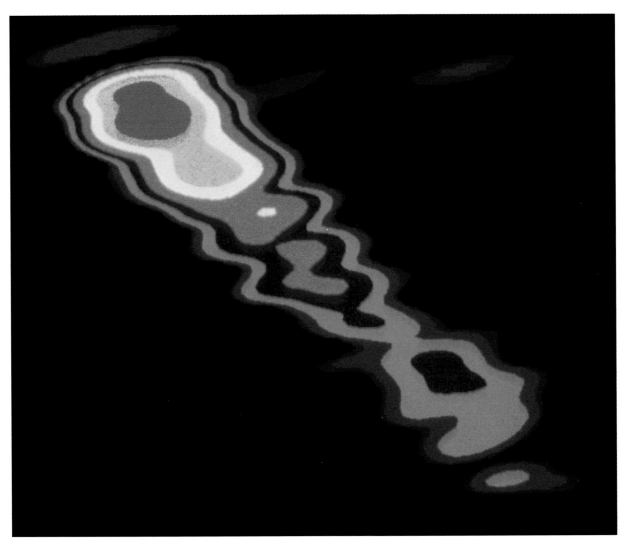

The most exotic object in the universe – a quasar. This is an image from a radio telescope of the quasar 3C 273 showing the quasar itself (red) and an enormous jet which extends an estimated 1.2 million light years from its nucleus. 3C 273 is the closest known quasar, some 2100 million light years away.

QUASARS

In 1963, an astronomer at the Palomar Observatory in California was studying what appeared to be a star. The object seemed to be in the same position as a radio source, identified by the exciting name of 3C273, and when its spectrum was analysed it could be seen that the radio emissions were in fact light that had been enormously red-shifted.

A red shift could be caused by a gravitational field, but in this case the effect was far too great and could only be due to the speed at which the object was moving way from us. By applying Hubble's Law to the observed red shift, it was found that this object was at an extreme distance from us – much further than many galaxies.

Because the object looked like a star, but obviously wasn't because of its distance, it was called a "quasi-stellar object", or quasar, for short.

To be so bright, and yet still visible at such a vast distance, it was evident that the quasar was emitting enormous amounts of energy – far greater than in the case of an entire galaxy.

As more and more of these objects were discovered, it became clear that they were even more exotic than had first been thought. Most quasars are at much greater distances than ordinary galaxies, and are therefore much older. The distance of some of the furthest is now thought to be as great as 15,000 million light years, so we are looking at objects whose light left them 15,000 million years ago; that means they are some of the oldest objects in the universe.

Apart from their great distance and age, quasars can vary the intensity of their light over relatively short periods, so cannot be very large for the amount of energy they emit. It is not known what power sources drive these extraordinary objects, but it is possible that they represent the earliest stages in the evolution of galaxies and contain supermassive black holes, formed from a mass equivalent to one hundred million suns.

COSMOLOGICAL THEORY

THE ENORMOUS SIZE OF the universe causes great problems for anyone attempting to explain its large-scale motion – across the vast distances of the universe it does not appear to change significantly over a human lifetime. Even galaxies – pinpoints in relation to the universe as a whole – continue in a state of equilibrium for many billions of years.

We may not be able to detect the movement of objects on an astronomical scale by direct observation, but analysis of the light coming from such objects does allow us to work out how they move relative to the Earth. The light from all galaxies outside the local group shows strong red shifts, as described earlier. These red shifts are indications that the galaxies are moving away from us.

If all objects, except those nearby, are moving apart, then the universe must be expanding. Some people still instinctively feel that we must be at the centre of the universe, just because everything appears to be moving away from us – in fact, there is no reason to suppose that we hold any special position at all.

The apparent motion of galaxies can be understood quite simply in terms of everyday experience. If you are travelling in a car, and your car is moving faster than another car behind you, then the two cars are moving apart despite the fact that they are moving in the same direction. Similarly, if a third car is in front of you and travelling faster, it will be moving away from your car. In fact, all three cars are moving apart, but they are still moving in the same direction.

Could this artist's impression really be correct – a big bang 15 billion years ago?

Another way to visualize the motion of galaxies is in terms of a ballon that is being blown up. If you draw a number of dots close together on the balloon's surface, as it expands the dots all move in roughly the same direction, away from the balloon's centre, but all are moving apart – look at the illustration on these pages. Imagine galaxies in much the same way – as if they are on an expanding surface – and it is easy to see why they appear to be moving away from each other.

So we have a picture of the universe in which there is a large-scale expansion. What we have to ask is this: if the universe is expanding, how did it come about and what will happen in the long-term future? A number of theories have been put forward about the beginning and evolution of the universe, and the three that have enjoyed the most popularity over the last few decades are described below.

1. THE STEADY STATE THEORY

The term "steady state" is rather misleading, because it suggests that the universe is unchanging. This is not the case because this theory accepts that the universe is expanding. In this context, "steady state" refers to the idea that the universe has always existed and will continue to exist for all time, extending infinitely out into space.

However, if the universe is expanding then it would "thin out" with time, and this theory proposes that new matter is spontaneously created in the space left by receding galaxies. The matter then forms new galaxies to fill the space caused by the expansion of the universe.

At one time, the Steady State Theory was supported by a number of eminent theoreticians, but it was never generally accepted and is no longer considered viable.

2. THE OSCILLATING UNIVERSE

This is a variation on the Big Bang Theory, below, which holds that the universe began with an explosion from a point in space, and will expand to a certain size before contracting back to the original point. The cycle will then be repeated and the universe will "oscillate" between its point source and its maximum radius. Like the Steady State Theory, this is no longer widely held.

3. THE BIG BANG THEORY

This is the theory of the origin and evolution of the universe that is currently popular. It assumes that all the

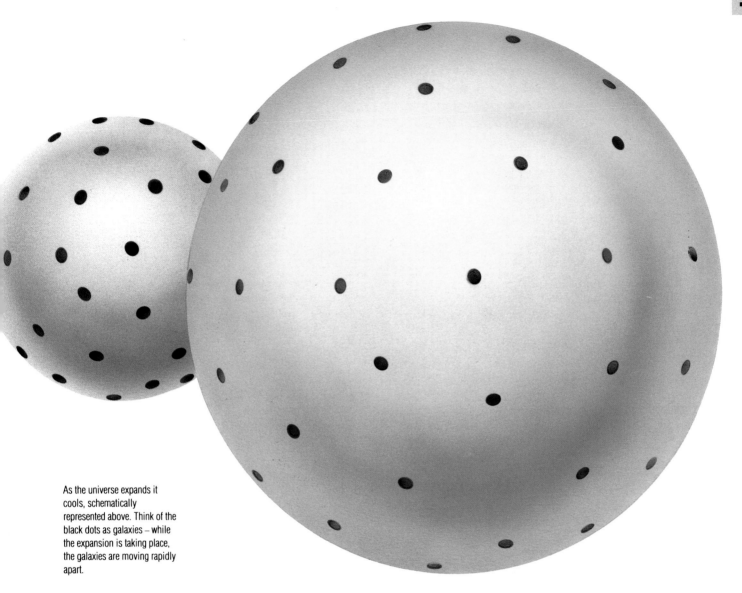

As the universe expands it cools, schematically represented above. Think of the black dots as galaxies – while the expansion is taking place, the galaxies are moving rapidly apart.

matter that exists in the universe today was once at a single point, that this exploded in a "big bang", and that the expansion we see today is the result of that explosion.

The moment of the big bang itself is considered to be the beginning of the universe, and time is measured from that moment. Immediately after the explosion, all matter existed in the form of "elementary" particles, the smallest possible constituents of all material things.

At this time, the theory has it, the universe was still compressed into a relatively small area, and was immensely hot. As the universe expanded and cooled, the simplest elements – hydrogen and helium – began to form, perhaps 300,000 years after the big bang.

Next we jump an incredible period of time – hundreds of millions of years. During this time, the hot, early universe has changed enormously. Local variations in density have caused enormous clouds of gas to form and in these the galaxies begin to develop, with billions of stars shining for the first time.

The largest and densest of these new galaxies may have formed supermassive black holes in their nuclei. Fuelled by the enormous amounts of free matter, these galaxy/black hole combinations shine more brightly than anything else in the universe – they are quasars. But the rate at which these objects use fuel means that they do

not survive past the infant stages of the universe, and are only seen today as relics of the past.

A snapshot taken five billion years after the big bang, shows the quasars to be less prominent, though there is still a wide variety of activity. Galaxies are forming in all sorts of shapes and a universe not unlike the one we see today is developing. But the universe is still expanding, and does not look like stopping. If there is not sufficient matter, then the galaxies will continue to increase their separation, eventually using up all their star-building material, and in time the universe will become dissipated, cold and dead.

Later, though, the rate of expansion seems to be slowing down, and the assumption is that this is the result of mutual gravitational attraction of the matter in the universe. However, as we study that matter it becomes evident that only a tiny percentage of the amount needed to explain the slowing process can be seen. It appears that at least ninety per cent, maybe more, of all matter is in some form that we cannot defeat.

So we reach the present day, at least 15,000 million years after the big bang. We still don't know if our cosmos will continue expanding forever, or whether it will collapse back upon itself – the "big crunch" at the end of the universe.

FUTURE SPACE TRAVEL

SINCE THE DAWN OF the space age in 1957, with the first successful launch of an artificial satellite, humanity has raced outwards into the Solar System. It seems as if there is no stopping us – the inhabitants of the third planet around the Sun. Already men have landed on the Moon, a quarter of a million miles away, and space probes have travelled to the outermost planets.

But what of the future? How and where will our next step take us? Look at the terrestrial planets, our nearest neighbours beyond the Moon: Venus, at its closest, only about 40 million miles away; Mars, roughly 60 million; Mercury, around 80 million miles. But would we want to send someone to these planets? Mercury is so close to the Sun that the radiation levels are dangerously high. Venus, because of the greenhouse effect of its atmosphere, is too hot for a human being to survive. And even Mars, the most hospitable planet after Earth, is far enough away that a journey there and back would take six months to a year – an uncomfortably long time in the hostile environment of interplanetary space.

Nevertheless, it is probably Mars that would be the first target – possibly for a permanent settlement. The other inner planets can be studied by further unmanned probes, should scientists want to study them more.

But why do human beings want to expose themselves to the unpleasantness of space flight? Is it for our own personal satisfaction, just to show that it can be done? Is there some great prize awaiting us when we reach our goal? And what is the ultimate goal?

In exploring the planets, we on Earth can at least participate in the excitement of the voyage. We can listen to astronauts describing their fascinating experiences; we can share in the thrill of someone setting foot on another world. But what of greater challenges: the stars? Can we ever hope to reach them, and could we return?

Before we even consider such an undertaking we must look at the problems involved. The most obvious one is the distance that must be covered, even to the nearest of our interstellar group. To appreciate the vastness of space, compare what has already been achieved with what we are proposing.

The journey to the Moon, on an Apollo spacecraft, took about three days. To cover the same distance, light (or any other form of electromagnetic radiation) takes about one and a quarter seconds. To reach the outermost planets, light has to travel for about 12 hours. To cover the distance to the nearest star, Proxima Centauri, light takes over four years.

In 1905, Albert Einstein produced the Special Theory of Relativity, in which he showed that nothing could travel faster than the speed of light, and that it would in fact take an infinite amount of energy to reach that speed. Nevertheless, it is theoretically possible to get near to the speed of light, so interstellar travel might be possible, albeit very time-consuming.

If we assume that we could produce a spaceship capable of reaching such heady speeds, why not do it? There are one or two considerations that might well affect our enthusiasm for such a venture. First, we cannot just turn on our engines and dash off at nearly light speed – we have to accelerate gently, so that the crew of the spaceship survive to tell the tale. This might take a year or so, and, of course, we have to slow down at the other end – another year added to the flight time. That means a trip to Proxima Centauri and back is going to take ten years or so.

Also, to achieve a high percentage of the speed of light is going to take a huge amount of energy – even a small ship might require several times the amount of energy generated on Earth in a year. This raises the problem of how to generate the energy, and where to store the fuel.

But assume that the problems of energy generation can be overcome and some intrepid astronauts head off towards Proxima Centauri. An interesting effect, predicted by the Special Theory of Relativity, is that as they approach the speed of light, time will move more slowly for them than for people back on Earth. This effect is known as time dilation. It is a particularly useful by-product of travelling very fast, as it means that the journey will take far less time than one would expect – at least for the astronauts themselves. Back on Earth, the trip will appear to take the full ten years.

But the effect is greater the nearer one approaches light speed, and increases the longer spent at that speed. An unfortunate consequence is that astronauts, who may be away for what seems to them to be a few decades, would arrive back on Earth to discover that everyone they knew had been dead for generations.

Looking at all of the problems associated with interstellar travel, it must be debatable whether we will ever leave our own Solar System. And, of course, to look again at an earlier question, "can we ever hope to reach the stars, and return?" – who would want to travel on a journey knowing that they would never see their family or friends again?

But perhaps there is a way for the human race to populate the rest of the Galaxy. One day a giant spacecraft might be built, large enough to hold thousands of people, travelling slowly through the interstellar void, generation after generation, never to return to Earth. These space-age explorers might one day find other worlds, crossing the vast oceans of space in the same spirit that led Christopher Columbus to cross the Atlantic, five hundred years ago.

OTHER WORLDS, OTHER LIVES

YOU HAVE ALREADY SEEN a little of the staggering variety and beauty of the universe. From our own familiar neighbours in the Solar System you have travelled through the cosmos to the edges of space and time. Some of the objects encountered stagger the imagination, almost to the point of disbelief.

But among this diversity there seems to be order. Scientists believe they can now, or will soon be able to, predict the evolution of stars, galaxies and even the universe itself. Why then do we seem to be alone in the universe? When everything about us has formed as a natural consequence of the laws that have governed the cosmos since the Big Bang, why is Earth the only planet on which life has risen from the primordial soup?

Can it really be that nowhere else, on the countless planets that surely must exist in the universe, are there civilisations that also look into the sky and wonder what life is out there? To believe that we are the only beings in this galaxy, let alone in the entire universe, is no less egocentric than the long-held notion that we are at the centre of creation. Even if the advent of life on Earth was an accident, rather than a commonplace occurrence, the probability must surely be that the same accident has occurred somewhere else. And if it has, why should we expect to have our interstellar neighbours use massive resources to visit us? Perhaps they don't know we exist. Perhaps they have contacted us, but we are too primitive to understand. Perhaps they do know we exist, but see no reason to talk.

If we look at the situation from a practical point of view we might understand why we do not hear anything. We have only been making our presence known, in the form of radio and TV broadcasts, during the few years of this century. So our signals have travelled less than 100 light years into space. Within this distance there may be no other civilisations to hear us. Even if there are, it is unlikely that they could receive such weak signals. So nobody knows we are here, and without good reason to travel the vast distances between the stars it seems improbable that anyone would just drop in for a visit. Even if this were the case, since we have only been on this planet for a very short time in the life of the universe, our alien neighbours might have passed this way long before we existed. After all, the universe has been going for some 15 billion years.

Of course, simply because we haven't been aware of it doesn't necessarily mean that other life forms have not been here recently. With our usual sense of self-importance humans assume that other beings would actually want to communicate with us. It may well be that a civilisation advanced enough to travel between the stars would arrive here simply to study us, just as we do with lower forms of life on Earth. They might find us quite amusing as examples of primitive life, but see no point in letting us know of their existence.

Whatever the truth of the matter, we are definitely beginners in the game of galactic conversation, and it may be that interstellar communication is something that is always to be denied us. Perhaps no species survives long enough to cross the voids in space. Probably we shall never know if someone else is out there.

The possibility that we may never reach the stars is rather depressing. Thoughts of the humanity being trapped on planet Earth, for the rest of its existence, seem to put an end to our insatiable quest for the unknown. But, as we have seen with many theories over the centuries, things change. Perhaps not tomorrow, or the next day, but sometime we may find a way to conquer the darkness that seems to close around us.

This star seen edge on, some 50 light years away, appears to be surrounded by a disk of material. Could this be the birth of a new planetary system?

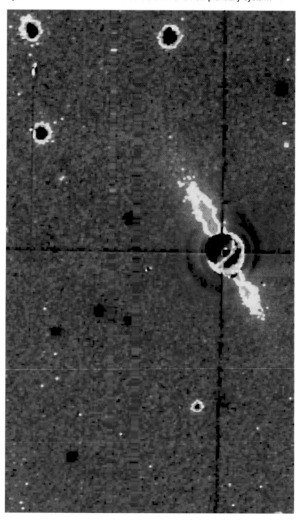

We shall certainly reach out into the Solar System, to the planets, and set up colonies in space. Perhaps we shall send great numbers of people, on giant spacecraft, on journeys of discovery through the interstellar void. Will we someday pack up and leave Earth entirely, looking for a better world, or worlds, to occupy, leaving the cradle of the human race behind, only to be remembered by historians, thousands of generations hence?

However our future unfolds there will never again be an era in which our views of the universe change so rapidly, and when the excitement of exploration can touch so many of us. More importantly, what we do now to understand the universe, and take our first cautious steps into it, may provide our only chance of survival when we reach the point at which the Earth's resources have been exhausted. When we no longer have a habitable planet there will still be an entire universe out there – but will we be capable reaching it?

The exploration of that universe begins with an understanding of our place in it. Reading this book you have taken your first steps toward that understanding, and to an appreciation of the scale of the cosmos. Just look at the skies on a dark evening and share the wonder that humanity has known for thousands of years. If you can turn away without some sense of awe at the majesty above you, then it must have been a cloudy night – take another look quickly, there may be only a few billion years left.

APPENDIX: ATOMIC PHYSICS

THE STUDY OF ASTRONOMY is concerned with the largest objects in existence. But everything in the universe – ourselves, the Earth, stars and galaxies – is made up of tiny particles, so small that no-one has ever seen them.

The study of these minute particles is the realm of atomic and nuclear physics, sometimes called particle physics. This sounds off-putting, but in fact it is fairly easy to reach a general understanding of the microscopic world of the atom.

This does depend, though, on working through a number of analogies. They may be useful – in fact, almost essential for understanding – but it is important to remember that they are not accurate representations of what is really going on. A definitive view demands an understanding of two branches of physics that are far too complex to describe here: Einstein's General Theory of Relativity, relating to the behaviour of large-scale objects in the universe; and quantum mechanics, concerned with atomic and sub-atomic particles.

So, back to analogies. All matter in the universe is made up of atoms: incredibly small objects in their own right, but not the smallest particles of all. Imagine the structure of the atom as a miniature Solar System: at the centre is an object with a relatively high mass called the nucleus, which itself consists of other particles; orbiting the nucleus are electrons, circling as the planets do around the Sun. (Electrons are familiar to us in everyday life – carrying one unit of negative electric charge, they are the source of electricity, creating an electric current as they jump between the atoms that go to make up wires and cables.)

The nucleus of an atom consists of smaller particles called protons and neutrons. Protons carry one unit of positive electric charge and, in a normal atom, the number of protons equals the the number of electrons. Because the negative charge on the electron is equal but opposite to the positive charge on the proton, such atoms are said to be electrically neutral. Despite this, though, a proton has nearly 2000 times more mass than an electron.

A neutron, the second type of particle in the nucleus, is made up of a proton and an electron, so has no overall electric charge. The mass of a neutron is very slightly greater than that of a proton, the difference being the mass of the electron.

But how many protons and neutrons are there in any particular atom? Every type of substance is made up of atoms, but obviously not all substances are the same: iron is different from lead; hydrogen is different from oxygen; and so on. These differences are caused by the varying numbers of protons in the nuclei of the substances.

In nature there are 92 different types of atoms, with each type having anything from 1 to 92 protons (and the same number of electrons) in its nucleus. These 92 different atoms are called the naturally occurring elements, each one with different chemical properties.

The simplest and lightest element in the universe is the gas, hydrogen. An atom of hydrogen has a nucleus consisting of only a single proton with no neutrons, with one solitary electron circling around it. The heaviest natural element, is uranium, with 92 protons and a swarm of 92 circling electrons.

This is all fairly straightforward. But, just to make things more difficult, the number of neutrons in the nucleus of many atoms is not always constant. In such cases, when a nucleus of one element has a different number of neutrons than is normal for that element, the atom is called an isotope of the element.

So far, we have described the structure of an atom in terms of a Solar System. Although this is not exactly how an atomic physicist might describe an atom it does at least give an idea of what is going on. But there is one major difference, apart from size, between the orbit of a planet and the orbit of an electron. A planet is constrained by gravity to move in a fixed orbit. An electron, though, can occupy any one of a number of discrete orbits around the nucleus – "discrete" here meaning that there are a number of fixed orbital distances from the nucleus, and the electron may not exist in any position between them. For any particular element these orbits are always the same, but different elements have different sets of fixed orbits.

Under normal conditions an electron occupies the lowest possible orbit (that is, the one nearest to the nucleus), but if the atom absorbs energy from any source then the electron may "jump" to a higher orbit. The more energy an atom absorbs, the higher the orbit that the electron adopts. But any orbit above the lowest one is an unnatural state for the electron, which will move back to a lower orbit as soon as it can. In order for this to happen, the atom must lose energy and this is achieved by the emission of a "packet" of energy from the electron. This packet is known as a photon, and the amount of energy it possesses is dependent upon the size of the jump made by the electron.

Since the size of the jump varies from one element to another, because of the difference in fixed orbits across the range of elements, the amount of energy contained in a photon is characteristic of the substance that emits it. That means that we can work out what element a photon comes from, and its place in the electromagnetic spectrum (*see p114*) by analysing the "colour" of its radiation – which is dictated by its energy level. There are X-ray photons, visible light photons, radio wave photons, micro wave photons and so on, for every part of the spectrum.

GLOSSARY

ABSOLUTE TEMPERATURE SCALE

A scale for measuring temperature whose lowest point is Absolute Zero. On this scale temperatures are followed by the letter K, after Lord Kelvin who first proposed the use of the scale, and degrees have the same magnitude as the Celsius, or centigrade, scale.

ABSOLUTE ZERO

The temperature of zero K, equivalent to –273.16 degrees C, at which all thermal motion in matter ceases and no heat remains.

ASTEROID

The word literally means "small star", but is now used to describe the numerous minor planets, most of which orbit the sun in a belt between Mars and Jupiter.

ASTRONOMICAL UNIT (AU)

The distance between the Earth and the Sun, equal to approximately 93 million miles (150 million kilometres), used as a measure of distance, mainly within the Solar System.

BARRED SPIRAL

A type of spiral galaxy that has a "bar" structure on either side of its nucleus. The spiral arms begin at the end of this central bar.

BIG BANG

A vast explosion at the beginning of the universe that is thought to have been the cause of the expansion that we observe today.

BIG CRUNCH

A theoretical end to the universe when all matter – stars, galaxies etc. – collapses to a single point in space.

BINARY STAR

Two stars that are orbiting about their common centre of gravity. These stars may be in actual physical contact or separated by as much as thousands of Astronomical Units. Some stars are referred to as "optical binaries", but these are not physically related and only appear close together because of a line-of-sight effect.

BLACK HOLE

The remains of a collapsed star that is so dense that the gravitational field around it is so intense that not even light can escape.

CELESTIAL EQUATOR

The projection of the Earth's equator onto the sky. This is used in star charts to divide the sky into northern and southern hemispheres.

CELESTIAL POLES

The projection of the Earth's north and south poles onto the sky.

CELESTIAL SPHERE

The imaginary sphere around the Earth on which ancient civilisations believed the stars to be fixed. The centre of this sphere is the same as the centre of the Earth. It is still convenient to use the celestial sphere today because it gives us a "surface" on which we can plot the positions of astronomical objects, and it is this surface that is represented by starcharts.

COSMOLOGY

The study of the universe, not only as it is today, but of its evolution in time and space.

CLUSTER OF GALAXIES

A group of galaxies that are held together by their mutual gravitational attraction. Clusters may contain from tens to hundreds of individual galaxies.

CONSTELLATION

A group of stars thought by ancient civilisations to represent mythical figures. Thre are 88 accepted constellations, which cover the entire sky.

DARK NEBULA

A cloud of cold dust and gas that does not emit or reflect light and is only detectable because it obscures the light of stars behind it. Sometimes known as an absorption nebula.

DECLINATION

The celestial equivalent of latitude on Earth. Declination is used to describe the position of an object north or south of the celestial equator, and is measured from 0 degrees (the celestial equator) to + 90 degrees at the celestial north pole and −90 degrees at the celestial south pole.

DOUBLE STAR

See Binary Star

ECLIPTIC

The projection of the Earth's orbit around the sun onto the sky, which therefore is also the apparent path of the Sun against the background of stars during the course of the year.

ELECTROMAGNETIC RADIATION

A form of energy that ranges from extremely high energy gamma rays, through x-rays, ultraviolet, visible light, infrared and microwaves, to radio waves. These are all types of electromagnetic radiation, varying only in their levels of energy.

ELECTROMAGNETIC SPECTRUM

The entire range of electromagnetic radiation, from high energy gamma rays to low energy radio waves.

ELLIPSE

The shape of the orbit of one object around another, described by Kepler's 3 laws of planetary motion.

EMISSION NEBULA

A cloud of gas and dust that is heated by stars within it. The cloud then radiates light with the characteristic colours of the elements within it.

EVENT HORIZON

The boundary around a black hole where the escape velocity is equal to the speed of light, and within which no event can ever be observed in the outside universe.

FINDERSCOPE

A small telescope, attached to an astronomical telescope, which has a wide field of view and which is used to aim the main telescope in the general area of the object which is to be observed.

GALACTIC CLUSTER
A cluster of stars found in the main disk of a galaxy, held loosely together by their mutual gravitational attraction, which will eventually break away from each other to become separate stars. Also known as "open" clusters.

GALAXY
A collection of billions of stars, gas and dust, held together by the force of gravity.

GAMMA RAYS
Electromagnetic radiation of very high energy.

GENERAL RELATIVITY
The theory proposed by Albert Einstein, which suggests that the laws of physics should be the same for all observers, regardless of the motion of the observer through space.

GLOBULAR CLUSTER
A spherical group of stars held tightly, and permanently, together by gravity. The stars in these clusters are very old and may have been some of the first to form in the galaxy.
Each cluster may contain hundreds of thousands, or even millions, of stars. Globular clusters are found in many galaxies, forming a spherical halo orbiting the nucleus of the galaxy. There are some 200 known in our Galaxy.

HYDROGEN
The simplest, and lightest, of all the elements. Hydrogen is also the most common element in the universe, and is the basic building block from which all stars are formed.

INFRARED
Electromagnetic radiation that has less energy than visible light.

LIGHT YEAR
The distance travelled by light in one year – approximately 6 million million miles (9.5 million million kilometres).

MAGNITUDE
A measure of the relative brightness of stars and other astronomical bodies. This system was originally created for stars that could be seen with the naked eye, and all such stars were given a magnitude from 1 to 6, according to their brightness, the brightest being magnitude 1, the faintest being magnitude 6. A star of first magnitude (magnitude 1) is about two and a half times brighter than a star of second magnitude (magnitude 2); a star of second magnitude is about two and a half times brighter than a star of third magnitude, and so on. There are some 20 stars which are brighter than first magnitude and these are given negative magnitudes, so that Sirius, the brightest star in the sky, is magnitude -1.4.

MASS
The quantity of matter in an object. The gravitational field of an object is directly proportional to its mass.

MERIDIAN
A circle on the celestial sphere that passes through the north and south celestial poles and the point directly overhead for the observer.

MESSIER'S CATALOGUE
A catalogue of 103 nebulae and clusters, observed by Charles Messier and published in 1784. Messier prepared this catalogue not because he was interested in nebulae and clusters, but because they could easily be confused with comets, which were his prime concern.

MILKY WAY
The name given by ancient civilisations to the band of light seen in the night sky that is caused by the light of millions of stars in our galaxy which are too far away to be seen as individual stars. The name is now generally used to describe our entire galaxy.

NEBULA
A cloud of gas and/or dust that may be seen because of light from nearby stars, or because it is cold and dark and obscures the light of objects behind it. The name "nebula" was

erroneously given to some distant galaxies in the last century, because these appeared as faint hazy patches, much like genuine nebulae, and nothing was known of galaxies outside our own at that time.

NEUTRON STAR
A star at the end of its life that has collapsed to extreme density (see Pulsar).

NEW GENERAL CATALOGUE (NGC)
A catalogue of nebulae and clusters observed by Sir John Herschel and published by Dreyer in 1888.

NOVA
The violent eruption of a star with the result that it becomes far brighter than normal for a period of a few days, weeks or months, before subsiding and returning to its former state.

OPEN CLUSTER
See Galactic Cluster.

PARALLAX
The apparent change in position of an object due to a change in the position of the observer. This is used to calculate the distances to some of the closest stars by observing their apparent change in position, against the background of distant stars, during the course of the year as the Earth moves around the Sun.

PARSEC
A measure of the distance that is defined as the distance at which a star would subtend a parallax of one second of arc across the radius of the Earth's orbit (see Parallax). The word Parsec is derived from the words of its definition, PARallax and SECond. The actual value of the Parsec is equivalent to approximately 3.26 light years.

PLANETARY NEBULA
A cloud of gas expanding away from a star, caused by the violent ejection of the outer layers of the star's atmosphere during the later stages of its life. This type of nebula was so named by 19th-century astronomers because the gas cloud appeared similar to a planet in their telescopes.

PROPER MOTION

The change in position of stars on the celestial sphere caused by the motion of individual stars through space.

PULSAR

A rotating neutron star emitting a powerful beam of radiation. Simply because it is rotating, the beam appears as pulses as it sweeps across the sky, creating the effect of a cosmic lighthouse.

QUASAR

Objects that appear star-like in telescopes, but are actually very distant and are travelling away from us at great speed. They emit vast amounts of energy and are thought to be the nuclei of galaxies in the process of formation early in the evolution of the universe. Their power source may possibly be supermassive black holes.

RED GIANT

A star in the later stages of its life when the atmosphere has cooled and expanded to many times its original size.

RED SHIFT

An effect on electromagnetic radiation caused by the recession of the source away from the observer. As the source moves away the radiation is "reddened", and the faster the source recedes, the greater the reddening effect. This effect is used to determine the rate at which distant galaxies and quasars are moving away from us, and hence the rate of expansion of the universe.

REFLECTION NEBULA

A cloud of gas and dust which is visible by the light it reflects from nearby stars.

REFLECTING TELESCOPE

A type of telescope design in which light passes down the telescope tube to the main, or primary, concave mirror at the rear. From here the light is focused onto a secondary mirror and reflected into the eyepiece.

REFRACTING TELESCOPE

In this type of telescope the incoming light is focused by a large object lens, at the front of the telescope tube, into an eyepiece at the other end.

RIGHT ASCENSION (RA)

The celestial equivalent of earthly longitude, measured around the celestial equator in divisions of hours and minutes, the equator being divided into a total of 24 hours.

SUPERNOVA

The explosion of a massive star in which the star may be totally destroyed. If the original star is not completely dissipated, then the core will collapse to form a neutron star or black hole. The most famous supernova remnant is the Crab nebula in the constellation of Taurus. This can be seen as a fast expanding cloud of gas with a rapidly rotating neutron star, or pulsar, as all that remains after the supernova explosion. For a short period, perhaps a few weeks, immediately after the explosion a supernova may outshine the combined light of all other stars in the galaxy.

VARIABLE STAR

A star whose brightness changes with time. The star may be intrinsically variable, such as a star that is unstable and expands and contracts with time, and may vary on a regular, semi-regular or irregular time scale. Another type of variable is due to a binary star system in which one star passes in front of the other in its orbit, and the total brightness of the pair changes as it does so. This is known as an eclipsing variable or eclipsing binary.

WHITE DWARF

A collapsed star, at the end of its lifetime, that is stable but generates no further energy of its own, and is radiating its heat away, eventually to become a black dwarf, cold and dark.

INDEX

FURTHER READING

Observing the Night Sky with Binoculars, Patrick Moore,
Cambridge University Press, 1986.

Turn Left at Orion, Guy Consolmagno and Dan M. Davis,
Cambridge University Press, 1989

Amateur Astronomy, Colin Ronan (consultant editor),
The Hamlyn Publishing Group, 1989

Observing the Constellations, John Sanford,
Mitchell Beazley International, 1989

Deep Time, David Darling,
Bantam Press, 1989

*Comets: A Chronological History of Observation, Science, Myth
and Folklore*, Donald K. Yeomans, John Wiley & Sons Ltd,
1991

ACKNOWLEDGEMENTS

All the photographs in this book, save those on pages 8/9, 14, 49 and 111 (which are courtesy of The British Library) are the property of The Science Photo Library, of 112 Westbourne Grove, London W2 5RU, Great Britain. Morgan Samuel Editions and Colin Humphrey would like to thank the staff of The Science Photo Library for their invaluable help during the preparation of this book.

Editorial & Production: Peter Price; Cheryl Jacob.
Design: Atkinson Duckett Consultants, London.
Art Director: Tony Paine.
Illustrations: Julian Baker, The Maltings Partnership, Derby.
Index: Harriet Ashworth.
Administration: Dr Jenny Sutcliffe.
Publisher: Nigel Perryman.